ALLEN COUNTY PUBLIC LIBRARY

3 1833 00  P9-EDT-150

The
Greatest Adventure

A STORY OF JACK LONDON

The
Greatest Adventure

A STORY OF JACK LONDON

by Frederick A. Lane

Illustrated by Sidney Quinn

ALADDIN BOOKS

New York: 1954

LIBRARY OF CONGRESS CATALOG CARD NUMBER: 54-6151

ALADDIN BOOKS IS A DIVISION OF AMERICAN BOOK COMPANY

COPYRIGHT, 1954, BY FREDERICK A. LANE. All rights reserved.
No part of this book protected by the above copyright may be
reproduced in any form (except by reviewers for the public
press), without written permission of publisher.   FIRST EDITION

PRINTED IN THE UNITED STATES OF AMERICA

Contents

CO. SCHOOLS

C386973

The
Greatest Adventure

A STORY OF JACK LONDON

The Oyster Pirates

📋 ON A BRIGHT SUNDAY MORNING in the spring of 1891, a boy walked westward through the city of Oakland toward San Francisco Bay. His steps quickened as he drew closer to the landing where he kept his skiff.

It was good, he thought, to be back on the waterfront after so many long months. He looked eagerly at the sealing schooners, the whalers, and sugar barks, whose tall masts were thrust skyward. Off the Oakland City Wharf, he could see a flock of smaller boats, belonging to the oyster men. The glittering water was alive with rowboats and sloops.

Riding high among the oyster sloops, out on the horizon, the boy's sharp eyes made out a Chinese junk.

He breathed deeply of the morning air, tangy with the sea smells. The raucous cry of a circling gull was music to his ears.

Beyond was the wide expanse of San Francisco Bay. The waters of the great harbor, whipped by a biting northwest wind, were laced with whitecaps.

The boy's gaze was held by a four-masted barkentine, disappearing behind Goat Island on her way to the Golden Gate, the outlet to the Pacific. Where, he wondered, was she bound? At what strange exciting ports would she touch? Was her lucky crew on the way to China, or Alaska, or the South Seas? He sighed. If only he were sailing with them on some great adventure . . .

As the barkentine vanished from his sight, the boy turned and started toward his little skiff. Today he would head for a cove he knew about and spend a few hours fishing. For a while he would try to forget the drudgery of the months past—and the drudgery of the months which lay ahead.

When he stepped onto the wharf where

his little boat was tied up, a familiar voice hailed: "Hey you, Jack London!"

The boy looked around and saw Pete, the Italian fisherman, who had sold him the skiff for six dollars nearly a year before.

Pete was seated on a bench in front of the wharf repairing a net. "A long time I don't see you, Jack. Where you been?"

"I've got a job, Pete," Jack replied. "I work in a cannery."

"A cannery, hey? What kind of work you do in that place?"

Jack explained. From seven each morning until late at night, he was in a hot, steamy world. A world of machines. He looked down at his hands, at the cuts he'd got while pitting fruits and cutting vegetables. Still, he was lucky. Some of the other boys and girls had lost fingers.

"All day long you do the same thing over and over?" Pete shook his head. "That's no kind of work for a boy who can sail a boat like you."

"It's steady money, Pete," Jack said quietly. "Ten cents an hour. On the days I work until midnight I make over a dollar and a half."

"And your family—they need the money.

Your papa—he can't work much any more, hey?"

Jack nodded. John London had been struck by an electric train. For a long time he would be able to do little work.

Pete rose and put a hand on the boy's shoulder. "That cannery is no good for you, Jack. Your eyes—they don't shine any more. Your face is not nice and brown. It has the same color as a flounder's belly. I think you feel dead in the head, too." He gestured toward the Bay. "Out there, on the water— that's where you should make the money."

Jack looked down at his skiff which was nudging the pilings. It would be good if he could make a living on the water—and Pete was right. He had been "dead in the head" for nearly a year. Why, he hadn't even been near the Oakland Public Library where he used to go nearly every day after school. He thought of the wonderful books Miss Coolbrith had helped him select, and wondered if she were still the librarian. The books Miss Coolbrith had shared with him had been more than printed words between covers. Each one had been a thrilling adventure, a door opening on the world. Those had been such fine days. But now, they were buried in the past.

After grammar school was over, life seemed to have become meaningless. The dull, endless work in the cannery left him no time except for eating and sleeping; it robbed him of every bit of energy. Rarely did he even feel like sailing his skiff on a Sunday.

"If I had a big boat, I would give you a job myself, Jack," the fisherman said. "But I have my own two boys, so—" He paused, then added, "maybe you can get a job on one of the ferryboats, hey?"

Jack shook his head. "They told me they didn't want fifteen-year-old boys. There are experienced men trying to get those jobs."

Pete pulled at his black mustache thoughtfully. "Times are hard. That's what everybody say—"

He broke off as a strongly accented voice rang out: " 'Ello, Pete."

Jack turned to see a dark, hawknosed man wearing a red shirt and a red bandanna around his head. A tingle of excitement shot through the boy's body. He knew the man swaggering toward them. He was French Frank, king of the East Bay oyster pirates.

French Frank halted and, hands on hips, grinned at Pete. "How's the fishing?"

"Fishing is all right," Pete answered.

"There is more money in oysters." The Frenchman laughed loudly. "Pete, you see that sloop out there—the one anchored near the sealing schooner?"

"I see her," Pete muttered. "She's your boat, *Razzle Dazzle*."

"That is right. And she is the fastest, best sloop in all of San Francisco Bay. Almost new she is. Built only two years ago—in1889. Pete, you listen!" French Frank shook a finger under the fisherman's nose. "I wish to sell my *Razzle Dazzle* because I am buying myself a schooner. Only three hundred dollars I am asking for that fine sloop."

"I got a boat," Pete said.

French Frank shrugged. "Maybe, you hear of someone, eh? That sloop—she is one gold mine for somebody with three hundred dollars cash. You see some smart fellow and you tell him, eh? I will be aboard all day."

With that, he strode off toward the end of the wharf. Jack watched the man jump into a dory and begin rowing out to his sloop. When the boy turned back to Pete he saw that the old man was frowning.

"Those fellows—they make plenty money, Jack. And they tell everyone they are not pirates. They say they dredge oysters from

only the old beds near Asparagus Island—beds nobody owns any more. But nighttime comes, they sneak down and scoop the fat oysters from the private beds. Next day, they sell them for twenty-five, maybe thirty dollars. But it is no good. They spend that money quick; they get in trouble. Sometime, they all go to prison."

Jack was hardly listening. He was staring intently at the sloop as she nodded her bows to the swells in the Bay.

Months before, when he had sold newspapers on the waterfront, he had often watched the oyster boats streaking up from the south to tie up at the Oakland City Wharf. He'd seen the men sell their catch to eager buyers.

Along with French Frank, the boy had come to recognize Harmonica Slim, Joe Goose, and Young Scratch Nelson and other waterfront pirates. To Jack, the laughing, carefree men were like the dashing adventurers he had read about in books. He had never dreamed of becoming one of them. But now . . .

His heart began pounding. Suppose—instead of a tiny skiff—he owned a craft like the *Razzle Dazzle*. He could live on the water; he could make the money his family needed so badly.

For a moment, Jack could almost feel the bite of wind and spray on his face. Then he let out a long breath. It was useless to think about such a thing.

As if from far away, he heard Pete saying: "Here, Jack. Take these sardines. Fine bait."

"Thanks, Pete."

"I saw you looking at that *Razzle Dazzle,* Jack," the fisherman said gently. "I know what is in your head. You think being an oyster pirate would be better than working in a cannery, hey?"

"Yes. Don't you think so too, Pete?"

Pete's brow furrowed. "I think fishing is good, but lawful fishing. Not poaching on other people's oyster beds. It is not good to make money too easy. It makes you weak and sick, deep inside, and you don't know about it until it is too late."

Jack stepped down into his skiff. Casting off the painter, he said with a crooked grin: "I guess I won't have to worry about that, Pete. I couldn't raise three dollars, let alone three hundred, to buy French Frank's sloop."

Jack shoved the skiff away from the pilings with an oar and began rowing out into the Estuary. Threading through the crowded shipping, he neared open water where he stepped his stubby mast and hauled up a patch of canvas. As the breeze blew him under the stern of the pirate craft, he looked up. Nobody was on deck, but smoke wisped up from the chimney of the *Razzle Dazzle's* cookstove. He heard a burst of raucous laughter drift from her cabin.

Three hundred dollars, he thought as he passed the sloop. It might just as well be three million.

Well out on the Bay, the sun was warm on Jack's back, but the cold northwest wind stung his face and brought tears to his eyes. Each passing moment put the cannery farther astern and his spirits began to lift.

The skiff slanted through the whitecaps as Jack guided her toward Goat Island. Skirting the island to the north, the little boat drew closer to San Francisco, the city where Jack had been born. He always thought of it as his city though he seldom put foot in it, nowadays. He could see the morning sun glittering on the spire of the Ferry Building and, along the waterfront, the clustered ships from all over the world.

Jack's gaze ranged the city's steep slopes, where the houses rose one above another. But he wasn't thinking about the bankers, or the railway and mine owners who lived in those stately mansions on Nob Hill. The names of quite different men came into his mind when he thought of San Francisco — Mark Twain, Bret Harte, Robert Louis Stevenson. They all had lived and worked in the city; other new and important writers were living there now. He stared at the city, a faraway look in his eyes.

"Stevenson's *Treasure Island* — What a great story that is," the boy said to himself, as he put into a little rockbound cove on the sheltered side of Goat Island. "Stevenson's pirates were the real thing—not just a bunch of oyster men."

He doused his sail and dropped anchor. Taking his fishing line from the locker, he baited his hooks with cut sardines. With his line out and looped around an oarlock, he stretched out in the bottom of the skiff, enjoying the warmth of the sun.

He stared up at the clouds scudding across the bright blue sky like hurrying sheep. He ought to have brought a book. He always used to have one with him. He closed his eyes and, as the skiff rocked gently, his thoughts wandered back to the days before he had graduated from grammar school.

There had been plenty of hard work then—but it was somehow different from toiling in a cannery. He had never minded getting out morning and evening to deliver papers, or running errands or sweeping stables on weekends to earn a few pennies. For, with all the work, there always had been moments when he could read.

Walking to and from school, during recess and lunch hours there was plenty of time for reading. And, on Sundays, when he would go fishing, he would bring along a book so that he could read while waiting for the fish to bite.

But once he had graduated from grammar school, life seemed to change overnight. If his father had not been hurt, things might have been different. Maybe high school would have been possible.

There was no hope of that, now. He had to help support the family. The light work his father could do, the music lessons his mother gave, didn't bring in enough money for food and clothes. Yet, as his mother had told him, there was no reason why he couldn't make something of himself. It was, she said, simply a matter of finding steady work and then making the most of his energy.

That is what she had said nearly a year ago and he had started out at the cannery with high spirits and high hopes. He had worked long hours and much harder than anyone else, but he didn't seem to be any better off than when he'd first started. It might be years before he'd get to be a foreman. Perhaps, never. He no longer cared very much. It seemed that all the ambition had been drained out of him.

The oarlock was rattling. Jack jerked erect and began hauling in on his line. He had a fish, all right. A big one, judging from the way it sulked down there. It was all he could do to drag it up from the depths—a big fellow with bulging eyes and a huge mouth. As it flopped on the bottom of the boat, Jack's eyes lit up. That rock cod weighed at least four pounds!

Quickly he baited up and dropped his line again. The sinker had hardly reached the bottom when he felt another jerk. He breathed excitedly. The fish were really hungry today.

Before they stopped biting, he had caught six fine rock cod, more than enough to take home. He would be able to bring some to his married sister, Eliza, and—to Jenny Prentiss.

"Mammy Jenny—" he whispered softly, remembering the kindly old nurse. He would stop by her house first. It would be good to see her again after all this time.

The northwest wind was stronger as Jack started back to Oakland, but he didn't reef his sail. Perched on the rail and gripping the tiller, he let the little skiff run. Off to starboard, came a lumbering ferryboat, her big sidewheels churning up the bay as she made her crossing to San Francisco. Grinning, Jack guided his craft into the wake of the ferry.

The skiff leaped and plunged like a wild creature. The ferry's passengers waved and Jack waved in answer. His laughter rang out as the spray stung his face, and suddenly he realized that it had been months since he had felt so wonderfully alive.

Golden Eagles

⊂≣ AS HE TURNED INTO JENNY Prentiss' yard, Jack was thinking about the *Razzle Dazzle*. He could not get the oyster sloop out of his mind. A craft like that would show her heels to anything that floated in all of San Francisco Bay. He could almost see himself at the helm with the spray flying and the wind filling the huge mainsail.

"Jack!" Jenny dashed out of the kitchen door and gave the boy a bear-like hug. She smiled broadly, her teeth flashing in contrast to her shining, dark brown face. "About time you came to see me," she exclaimed.

Releasing him, she stepped back and put her head to one side. "Lands' sake! You sure look skinny. I think you're working too hard at that cannery place. Trouble is, whatever you do, you put all your heart in it—whether it's sellin' papers or readin' books . . ."

Jack reached into his sack and drew out a fat fish.

"Rock cod!" the old woman chuckled. "I sure can eat my fill of baked rock cod." Then her laughter died away and a serious expression came over her face. "I just can't get over it, Jack. You are so peaked!" She took his arm and led him into the kitchen, saying, "Maybe, I can't fatten you up much, but I'll try."

While he sat at the kitchen table, Jenny made hot chocolate. She poured a cupful for him and gave him some hot corn bread spread with jam. "You eat every crumb, now," she ordered, as she took a chair opposite him. "Tell me all about how things are going at your house."

"Pa seems to be getting better. But he won't be able to do much work for a long time," Jack answered between mouthfuls.

Jenny nodded. "And Eliza? How's your

sister gettin' along with that army man she got married to?"

Jack reached for more corn bread. "Oh, 'Lize is very happy. Captain Shepard is a fine man."

The old woman leaned back. "Next," she said, "we comes to you, Jack. You've been workin' too hard, but that's only part of it. I want to know what's eatin' on you, deep inside."

"I'm all right."

"No, you ain't. Don't you try to fool me. Didn't I take care of you when you was little, all the time your ma was sick? Didn't I raise you up like you was my own boy? I know you inside and out, Jack London. Something's wrong. You got to tell me and maybe I can fix it."

Jack finished the last bit of cornbread. "There isn't anything you can do."

"Don't you talk like that! You tell me what's ailin' you. It's that cannery, ain't it?"

He stared down at the table. "I guess 1 wouldn't mind working there if—I could save some money. But at ten cents an hour—" He sighed. "I'll never be able to save up enough on that wage to buy a boat."

"You've got a boat," Jenny said. "What do you want another one for?"

"I'd like a big one. One I could make a living with—fishing, or dredging for oysters. A boat like . . ." He broke off. There was no use talking about it.

"A boat like what?" Jenny Prentiss demanded.

Jack told her of his meeting with French Frank. He described the *Razzle Dazzle* and the life he could lead if he owned her. "I could make enough money to really help my folks, and I'd have time to read and study, too."

"How much does that French Frank want for his boat?"

Jack shrugged. "More than I could make in a hundred years."

"How much?"

"Three hundred dollars," he murmured.

The old woman folded her arms. "Now you listen to me and don't you talk back. Tomorrow mornin', you go and quit that job you've got. Then you come here to my house. By that time, I'll be back from the bank and I'll have the money to give you."

Jack blinked.

"I mean it," Jenny said firmly. "I got the money."

The boy didn't know what to say. He knew it must have taken her years to save that much out of the wages she earned nursing and doing housework for people.

Finally, he stammered, "I—I can't take it, Mammy Jenny. I just couldn't."

"Didn't I tell you not to talk back to me, Jack London!"

"But I can't take your lifetime savings," he protested.

"What good is money if it can't help somebody? You come here tomorrow or else."

Jack hesitated. Then he remembered what Pete, the fisherman, had told him. The oyster-poachers made twenty-five, sometimes thirty dollars in a single day. At that rate, he would be able to make enough so as to pay his old nurse back before very long.

Thumping on the kitchen table, Jenny said, "That money will be here tomorrow morning. See that you're here, too. Or do you want me to have to go trudgin' all the way 'cross town to your house to give it to you?"

Jack grinned. "I'll come over here. But it will be a loan. I'll pay you back in no time."

*   *   *

Jack felt as though he were walking on air. He could hardly wait to tell Eliza the wonderful news. But when he came to his sister's house, he found no one at home. He left two fish in the woodshed, hung them on a string so that stray cats couldn't get them, and hurried home.

He began running as he neared the railroad tracks which passed by his family's house. He went up the porch stairs, two at a time. "Pa," he called out as he entered the little cottage.

"Your father isn't home, Jack." His mother spoke without looking up from her ironing. "He heard about a part time job and he went out to see about it. He's not well enough, but —he wouldn't listen to me."

"He's worried about money, Ma. But he won't have to worry any more!" The words tumbled out. He told about the *Razzle Dazzle* and Jenny Prentiss' offer to lend him the money to buy the sloop from French Frank.

"French Frank? I've heard about him." His mother put the iron aside and her brows drew together in a thoughtful frown. "And— I've heard about oyster piracy. Is that what you have in mind, son?"

"It isn't really piracy. Nobody pays any

attention to the oyster pirates. The police don't bother them. Anyway, I wouldn't go near the private beds. There are lots of abandoned beds where anybody can go."

"I don't know much about it," his mother said slowly. "But I do know you would be in bad company. I've read in the newspapers about French Frank and the others. They're a bad lot. Some of them have spent time in prison. I won't have you associating with them." A tired smile curved her lips. "We do need money, son, but—"

"You mean that I can't accept Jenny's loan?"

Flora London looked at her son silently. Only a few seconds before, he had been so alive—just the way he had been during his grammar school days. Now the dull look had come back into his eyes, the slump to his shoulders. The long months in the cannery had left their marks on him, and now, when he saw a way to break out of that deadly routine . . .

She pressed the back of her hand against her forehead, trying to make the right decision. It was true that the oyster pirates were a tough crowd, but—didn't her boy have a mind of his own? Hadn't she and John London so shaped his character that honesty and decency **were as** natural to him as breathing?

As if speaking to herself, she murmured, "It's not that I'm afraid you might do anything wrong, Jack. But you could get hurt. There is so much fighting along the waterfront."

"I won't get hurt. I've learned how to take care of myself."

His mother smiled slightly. It was very true that Jack had learned to defend himself. He'd had to. It was only by using his fists that he had been able to maintain his right to read during recess and lunch hour at school. When the boys called him "sissy" and tried to take his books away he had made it clear that Jack London was someone to let alone.

His mother came across the room and put her hand on the boy's arm. "It is very fine of Mrs. Prentiss to let you have the money," she said. "I suppose you plan to buy the *Razzle Dazzle* tomorrow morning?"

"Then — that means —" Jack swallowed hard. "You're not stopping me?"

"No, son. Go ahead with this new venture. I'll explain it all to your father when he comes home. He won't like it any better than **I do**, but I'm sure he'll understand."

*   *   *

Jack had trouble sleeping that night. He lay awake for a long time, excited by the thought of the adventurous life which would begin on the morrow. Then he began worrying. What did he know about oystering? He had an idea as to where the beds were located, but that was all. Still, he could learn, couldn't he? You could learn anything if you wanted to badly enough.

Next, he began wondering about who would be a good partner. Handling the sloop and the dredging was a two-man job. Since he had been working at the cannery, he had lost track of most of his friends. He thought of his school friend, Frank Atherton. Frank would be a fine shipmate, but he had gone to live on a ranch in Los Gatos.

Another thought nagged him: Suppose the *Razzle Dazzle* had been sold? Surely, a fine sloop like that wouldn't go begging for long.

Hours passed before he fell into a restless sleep from which he wakened with a start when the first pale glimmer of dawn streaked through his window. He dressed hastily, ran outside to bring in wood, started a fire, and cooked his own breakfast.

At five minutes of seven, Jack was in the

cannery, telling the foreman that he was quitting the job.

"Sorry to see you go," the foreman said. "It's not often we get a good steady worker like you.   Might be, I can talk the owners into giving you a bit of a raise if you'll stay on."

Jack shook his head.   "No, thanks.   I'm going to be my own boss.   I'm getting a sloop and am going into the oyster game."

"Oysters, eh?"   The foreman rubbed his chin.   "Heard about those fellows.   If I wasn't a married man with a family, I'd have a go at it myself."

Jack walked across town slowly.   There was no reason to hurry since the banks were not yet open.   He knew he would have to wait for Jenny Prentiss to withdraw her savings and get back home.

Nearing the Oakland City Hall on Fourteenth Street, he entered the park.   He sat down on a green wooden bench and looked across the street at the Public Library, remembering the happy hours he had once spent there.   Oystering wouldn't take up more than eight or ten hours a day.   Jack London, skipper of the sloop *Razzle Dazzle*, would have plenty of time for reading.

*   *   *

Mrs. Prentiss counted out the glittering coins on her kitchen table. They were golden eagles—ten dollar gold pieces. One by one she dropped them into a woolen stocking. Then, knotting it at the top, she handed it to Jack. "There you are, Jack. Three hundred dollars—and a little extra to buy things you might need."

Jack held the heavy stocking with trembling fingers. He looked at the kind old woman and tried to speak. "I—I simply don't know how to thank you, Mammy . . ."

"Never you mind thankin' me. You get right down to the docks and buy that boat off of French Frank." She almost pushed him out of the kitchen door. "Get on with you, now."

Outside, Jack began walking rapidly. Then he broke into a trot. Soon, he was running toward the Estuary, galloping past horse-drawn drays and startled porters.

Reaching the wharf, he looked out over the harbor, and stiffened. Where was the *Razzle Dazzle?* A big barkentine seemed to have taken her place in the harbor. Then the vessel shifted with the tide and Jack gave a sigh of relief. He could see that the sloop was still there.

But there were two men on deck and,

clearly, they were hauling up the anchor!

Leaping into his skiff, Jack put the stocking-ful of gold pieces in the stern locker and hastily cast off. His oars bit into the sun-streaked water as he sent the skiff skimming past the crowded shipping. He glanced back over his shoulder.

The sloop was making sail!

"Ahoy, the *Razzle Dazzle*," he shouted, re-doubling his efforts with the oars. "Ahoy, the *Razzle Dazzle!*"

The Razzle Dazzle

⚓ AS HE DREW CLOSER TO THE *Razzle Dazzle,* Jack heard French Frank shout: "Belay, Spider. Someone wants to come aboard." The oyster pirate glared down suspiciously as the skiff came alongside. "What you want?"

"I—I—" Breathless from the hard rowing, Jack couldn't talk.

"Speak up," French Frank growled. "I'm a busy man."

"I—I've come to buy your sloop, sir," Jack managed. "That is—if she's still for sale."

"So?" French Frank's manner changed.

With a quick smile, he said, *"Razzle Dazzle* is for sale. Cash money. Three hundred dollar. You got that much?"

"Yes, I have the money. I've got it with me. I—"

"Then, come aboard." French Frank leaned down. "Here, give me the painter. I make you fast."

With the skiff secure, Jack took the stockingful of goldpieces from the locker and then climbed aboard the sloop. Quickly he glanced around, drinking in the beauty of the neat craft. The cockpit from which the tiller was manned was lower than the rest of the deck. Just forward of the cockpit was a covered hatchway which led to the cabin below.

Jack had time for only a hurried look around, as French Frank dropped the anchor again and ordered the deckhand to furl the mainsail. "Now," he said, turning to Jack, "we go below and talk business."

Jack followed the oyster pirate down the hatchway ladder and found himself in the cabin. It was small, hardly half as large as his room at home, and every inch of space was being used. Yet it was not the least bit cluttered. Everything was shipshape, neat as a pin.

Aft and amidships was a small, potbellied stove. Near it was a rack for plates. Coffee mugs hung from hooks, as did various pots and pans. Over the woodbox was a basin for water and, near the basin, a hand pump.

There were two bunks, one on each side of the cabin. When they were not being used as beds, they served as benches for a folding table which could be swung down when needed. From overhead, in the center of the cabin, an oil lamp swayed from a crane.

French Frank put some wood into the stove and, drawing some water, filled a coffeepot. Glancing back over his shoulder, he said, "Sit down on that bunk. Now—you know me, French Frank. Everybody knows me on the waterfront. But I don't know you. I see you sailing that little skiff sometimes, but I don't know your name."

Jack told the oyster pirate who he was and French Frank, taking a can of coffee from the locker, nodded. "So! I know you can handle your skiff fine and someday you make a good sailor. But a little skiff is not like *Razzle Dazzle*. You know that?"

"I know," Jack said. "Still, I'm sure I can learn to handle her." As he spoke, his eyes were intent upon the gear which was all around him. There were sea boots, oilskin, and sou'westers—all in their proper places. There was a chart rack and near it, the compass and the signal flags.

As French Frank unhooked the table and swung it down between the bunks, he said with a chuckle: "Sure, you can learn. But you can't sail *Razzle Dazzle* all by yourself— and catch oysters, too. *Razzle Dazzle* is too big for one man."

"I was thinking," Jack said, "that maybe I could get a partner to go shares. Someone who knows the ropes and—"

"Now you talk sense." French Frank took two mugs from their hooks and put them on the table. The smell of coffee filled the cabin. From a food locker, he brought out a loaf of bread and some slices of cold beef. Then he sat down. "I will sell you *Razzle Dazzle*, Jack."

"I have the money here, sir." Jack began unknotting the stocking. "I guess you'll want to count it."

"No. I will not take the money now. First, we eat. After that, we go ashore and make bill of sale, all proper with witness. Then I

e the money and the *Razzle Dazzle* is yours.
Now, you need partner. You like me to get
you one?"

"Yes, sir. I certainly would. Do you know
of anybody?" Jack asked eagerly.

French Frank rose, smiling. "Maybe," he
said, "I get you someone—" he snapped his
fingers, "like that." Then, through cupped
hands, he yelled up the hatchway: "Spider!
Hey you, Spider. Come below!"

Sitting down again, he went on: "Spider's
good sailor. Lazy, sometimes, but you watch
him and he works good."

Presently a pair of long legs clad in sea boots
appeared on the ladder. The legs were attached to a long-nosed youth, his black hair
tied back under a red bandanna.

"Spider," French Frank ordered, "first you
shake hands with Jack London who will soon
own *Razzle Dazzle*. Jack, you meet Spider
Healey."

Silently Spider put out his hand and French
Frank continued: "Now, get yourself a cup of
coffee, Spider. Then we talk."

Jack wasn't very much impressed by Spider
Healey. He didn't like the limp handshake
or the young man's shifty eyes. However, he
couldn't afford to be choosy about a deckhand.

Spider, if he took the job, would have to do for a while, at least.

"Spider," French Frank said, "today I sell *Razzle Dazzle* to this Jack London and then I go upriver to look for a schooner—so you don't have a job. You want to stay in *Razzle Dazzle* and be Jack's deckhand?"

Spider, humped over his coffee cup, shrugged. "Sure," he muttered. "I don't care who I work for so long as I get paid."

"I can't pay you a regular wage," Jack said hurriedly. "But I'd be willing to give you a share in the profits from oystering. You see, after paying for the *Razzle Dazzle*, I'll have just enough left over to buy boots and supplies."

Spider grunted. "Well, give me plenty of grub and I'm your man."

French Frank finished his coffee and rose. "It is agreed, then," he said. "Now, Jack, we go ashore, and—" he grinned, "pretty soon, you own the finest sloop in all San Francisco Bay."

*   *   *

The deal completed, Jack hurried home. He stayed there just long enough to get some clothes, his few books, and to tell his mother: "I'm sleeping aboard my ship. Have to get the *Razzle Dazzle* ready to sail for the oyster beds at dawn."

A ship chandler saw him next. Captain Jack London of the *Razzle Dazzle* needed sea boots, oilskins, and a sou'wester. Then to the general store. The sloop *Razzle Dazzle* was taking on supplies for a voyage, he told the owner importantly. He'd need a sack of potatoes and one of onions. Also, a side of bacon, some coffee, and sugar.

Jack had only a few silver coins left when he piled his supplies and sea-gear into his skiff and headed for the sloop. As he rowed, he peered over his shoulder from time to time, feasting his eyes on the beautiful craft which now belonged to him. "Careful now," he muttered aloud as he drew close. "Stay clear or you'll scratch the paintwork." Then he called: "Ahoy, *Razzle Dazzle*. Hey, Spider, lend a hand with these supplies."

Spider appeared and looked down. "A good thing you stocked up," he said drily. "French Frank took everything in his dory that wasn't nailed down."

After stowing the supplies below in their proper places, Jack put his books on the shelf over his bunk.

Spider frowned, "Can you read them books?"

Jack refused to notice the frown and answered eagerly, "Some day, I'm going to have a big house all my own and—when I do—the walls will be shelves and the shelves will be crammed with books."

Spider shrugged. "Everybody's different, I guess. Me, I never learned to read or write. I just don't see the sense in it."

"But didn't you learn in school?" Jack asked.

"School? I never went to no school. I had no folks to send me. They died from fever when I was litle. Big Nick, a Greek fisherman, took me in. When he got drowned in a storm, I was on my own."

Jack felt sorry for Spider, but he couldn't understand how anyone who went to sea could help turning to books. The precious hours of freedom afforded by life on the water seemed just meant for reading.

When the cabin was shipshape, Jack said, "I want to look *Razzle Dazzle* over and get the feel of her. Then we'll take her for a run on the bay."

He spent the next hour going over every inch of the sloop from stem to stern. He wanted to learn every rope by which the jib and mainsail were managed, and he soon found out that Spider, even if he had no book-learning, seemed to be a good sailor. The canvas was neatly furled and secured. Halliards were coiled down. The metal brightwork gleamed, and the decks were spotless.

Jack asked about some iron contraptions with nets attached and Spider explained: "Them's oyster dredges. We use 'em in the deepwater beds down by Asparagus Island."

"Then we'll be using them in the morning," Jack said. He glanced out at the choppy, white-capped bay. "Let's get some canvas on her and we'll take her around Goat Island, then run south."

They hauled up the huge mainsail, dragged up the anchor, set the jib, and the *Razzle Dazzle* came alive. The sloop was sailing close-hauled on the port tack. Jack, manning the tiller, trembled with excitement. As he felt the wind-driven spray on his face, he shouted aloud from sheer joy.

Spider did his share of the work without any expression of pleasure. To him, sailing the sloop was just another job. When it came time to tack, he was at the mainsheet helping to haul the main boom amidships. Seconds later, he was forward, easing the jib sheet and hauling it aft as the sloop came around.

The *Razzle Dazzle* rounded Goat Island and with the wind aft, streaked southward. Spider, dropping into the cockpit said, "She's shippin' some water. You want to reef?"

Jack, his face flushed with excitement, shook his head. "Let her run. You take the tiller, Spider. I'll be your deckhand for a while."

Late that afternoon, when the *Razzle Dazzle* stood into her anchorage off the Oakland Estuary, Spider said admiringly: "Maybe you ain't handled anything bigger'n a skiff, Jack, but you sure got the feel of sailorin'. Won't be long 'fore you're as good as Young Scratch Nelson. He's got the *Reindeer,* a sloop just like this one. He's a driver, Nelson is. Never reefs down."

When the sails were furled, water bailed out, and lines coiled, they went below for supper. It was simple fare, but Jack thought he had never tasted better food.

As soon as the dishes were washed and put away, Spider turned in and fell asleep. Jack lit the oil lamp over his bunk and took a book from the shelf. It was the story of an Italian boy who became a great musician. It was

Jack's favorite book and he never tired of reading it.

The eventful day through which he had lived, faded from his thoughts. Even that thrilling tomorrow, when the *Razzle Dazzle* would make sail and head for the oyster beds off Asparagus Island—even that was not very important. He had lost himself in the struggles of the Italian orphan who wanted to make music.

The Winds of Adventure

⚓ IN THE MURKY DAWN, JACK guided the *Razzle Dazzle* while Spider took soundings with the hand leadline. Dead ahead lay Asparagus Island where the surf broke on a long, sandy beach. A few small craft could be seen, but they were far away.

Jack glanced up at the overcast sky. He sniffed the southeast wind. A day like this, he knew, could blow up a howling gale. He glanced at Spider, who looked just as sulky as he had an hour earlier. That was when he had said, "You're the boss, of course, but you better listen to me, Jack. You won't make no money out of them abandoned oyster beds."

"I don't expect to make anything like thirty dollars a day," Jack had replied.

"You sure won't," his partner had muttered.

Now, as the sloop neared the oyster beds, Jack was thinking that if they could make ten dollars a day, everything would work out all right. During the next few months, he would set the larger portion of his profits aside in order to pay back Jenny Prentiss. Then, later—

Spider's voice rang out. "Hard shell bottom. This is the place."

Lashing the tiller, Jack gave Spider a hand getting the heavy dredges over the stern, one to port, the other to starboard. The lines tautened as the sloop took up the slack and steadied to her work. Soon the iron hooks were biting into the floor of the bay. Jack hoped they were tearing off the fat oysters which would bring a good price in Oakland.

"Time to haul in," Spider muttered after a while. "I'll need help. Them dredges is heavy."

Together they laid hold of the starboard dredge rope and Jack panted, "Judging by the weight, Spider, that net ought to be crammed with oysters."

Spider growled sulkily. "You'll learn," he said. "You'll learn."

When the dredge was heaved into the cockpit and the contents of the net dumped out, Jack understood what Spider had meant. The catch was mostly mud mixed with small crabs and tiny oysters. Jack found only two of the shellfish large enough to be sold.

"Better luck next time, Spider," he said with a worried grin, as they let the dredge go over the stern and turned to haul up the other one.

The second dredge brought up no richer returns than the first. And then, reaching the end of the beds, they hauled both dredges aboard and brought the *Razzle Dazzle* around to cross the beds on a new course. They worked for several hours until the cockpit was so filled with mud that they had to call a halt to clean it out.

"Dredging these old beds," Spider grumbled, "is what I call hard work."

Jack, staring at the sack which contained only a few dozen big oysters, agreed. Yet he didn't mind the work. In fact he liked it, but he was beginning to wonder how, at this rate, he would ever be able to pay back the money he had borrowed.

He said slowly: "Spider, we've worked three

hours to get about a dollar's worth of oysters."

"I been tryin' to tell you this idea of yours wasn't any good," his partner broke in. "Why do you think the people who used to own this bed gave up workin' here? I'll tell you why. 'Cause they couldn't make nothin'."

"Still, French Frank and Nelson and some of the others come here regularly," Jack said.

Spider laughed raucously. "That's only a bluff to make folks think they ain't poachin'. They come here durin' the day. At night, they raid the private beds. That's what we're goin' to have to do if we expect to make any money."

"But it's wrong," Jack protested. "It's against the law."

Spider shrugged his narrow shoulders. "Depends on how you look at it," he said. "A couple of big companies own all them oyster beds. They keep the price up so high on oysters, only rich folks can afford to eat 'em. If it wasn't for the pirates, lots of people would never know what oysters tasted like."

The *Razzle Dazzle* heeled over as a sudden gust of wind struck her. "She's blowing up," Jack said. "Let's get back to work before it gets any worse."

"Look here," Spider growled, "I ain't goin'

to kill myself for a few oysters no matter what you . . ."

"All right," Jack said shortly. "Take the tiller. I'll handle the dredges myself."

With the increasing wind, the sloop was harder to handle, but she was covering more ground. It was all Jack could do to pull in the dredges, one after the other, and pick out the big oysters. But he kept at it until his back was aching and his arms felt as though they were pulling out of their sockets.

By noon, a near gale was blowing, whipping the bay into a froth. Jack pulled in his dredges for the last time. When the cockpit was clean, he gazed with satisfaction on a nearly full sack of oysters and said: "We'll go in now, Spider. If the gale blows out, we'll come back."

Spider looked at him with bulging eyes. "I got to admit you can take a lot of punishment. I never did see anyone work like you do—" He broke off suddenly, pointing. "There he comes. Young Scratch Nelson in the *Reindeer*."

Jack looked over the starboard bow to see a sloop bearing down. With all canvas up, she sent the spray flying as she plunged through the swells like a wild creature. The craft kept coming closer.

Jack shouted: "He's crazy, Spider. He's trying to run us down."

"Naw. He'll come close, but he won't ram us. You watch."

Wide-eyed, heart in mouth, Jack stared as the sloop drew nearer and then swept by, purposefully missing the *Razzle Dazzle* by inches. At the *Reindeer's* tiller stood a blond young giant whose laughter rang out as he went by. Jack watched until he saw the sloop's jib flatten, her main boom swing as she tore off on a new tack and streaked southward.

"What a sailor!" Jack said admiringly.

"Yep. Ain't nobody can touch Young Scratch when it comes to sailin'. He's named after his pa who's called 'Old Scratch' on account of the way he claws when he gets in a fight." Spider grinned crookedly. "Young Scratch is headed for them private beds down below Asparagus Island. Raids 'em in broad daylight, he does. When the watchmen start shootin' at him, he just laughs. He ain't scared of nothin'."

"He's a great sailor," Jack said as the *Reindeer* became a speck in the distance. "But give me time to get used to *Razzle Dazzle* and I think I could give him a race."

"That," said Spider as the sloop got under way and headed for Oakland, "is something I'd like to see."

With the *Razzle Dazzle* anchored in the Estuary, Jack took the sack of oysters ashore in his skiff. A half hour later, he was back aboard, having sold the catch to a hotel man for six dollars. He set aside the sum he had paid out for food and gave Spider a third of the rest.

The thought came to him that, as owner of the sloop, he was responsible for her upkeep. She would need paint from time to time, and worn-out rope and canvas would have to be replaced. He would have to make more than six dollars a day if he expected to keep the *Razzle Dazzle* in repair, repay his debt to Jenny, and help out his family.

Late that afternoon, he saw the *Reindeer* blow in. Running past the shipping, she headed for the City pier. Her jib fluttered down, then her mainsail, as she slid neatly alongside the wharf. The lines went over and she was made fast. Soon, bulging sacks were being passed up from the sloop to the wharf. Clearly,

Young Scratch Nelson had done well for himself that day.

At supper in the cabin that evening, Jack asked, "Spider, are there other abandoned oyster beds like the one we worked today?"

"Sure. There's a few. Most of 'em pretty well thinned out, though." Spider bent over his plate. His shifty eyes did not meet Jack's. "Might be, we could do better in the lower bay. Down Millbrae way—that's where the shallow beds are. You got to have low tides so you can get on 'em."

"There are low tides in the early morning starting next week," Jack said.

"That's right! I forgot all about 'em," Spider exclaimed.

Jack looked at him, puzzled. Fishermen always remembered tides. He might have wondered about it had not Spider gone on quickly: "We'll work the Asparagus Island beds until the tides are right. Then we'll have a try at the shallows in the lower bay."

*   *   *

During the days that followed, the *Razzle Dazzle* crisscrossed the oyster beds and Jack did most of the work. Spider did what he was told, but he seemed unable to match Jack's driving strength, and he was quite as lazy as French Frank had warned.

Each afternoon, when the northeast winds blew hard across the open stretch of bay, they came in, sold the oysters, and attended to the endless little repair jobs needed to maintain the sloop in good repair. Now and then, Jack took the skiff and rowed ashore to spend an evening at home. Then, after reassuring his worried parents, he would visit his sister Eliza or Jenny Prentiss. Occasionally, there was a little time to spare and he headed for the Oakland Public Library.

At night, Jack read the books which Miss Coolbrith had chosen: "This one, Jack, is by a promising new British author, Rudyard Kipling," the gentle librarian had said. "Also, take these short stories by Richard Harding Davis."

And so, for a while, Jack's life on the *Razzle Dazzle* was as wonderful as he had expected it would be. The hard work did not bother him now that he had time to read.

But, after six days, he was more worried than ever about his profits. He counted up his earnings and they came to a little over thirty dollars. Out of this amount, he had to pay for supplies, sea gear, new sacks—and give Spider his share. What was left over he divided between his mother and Jenny. But at this rate his earnings would not match his wages at the cannery. He hoped that the shallow beds in the lower bay would prove to be more profitable.

"You really think we'll do better there?" he asked, as he paid Spider.

Spider nodded and pocketing the money said, "Goin' ashore for a fling, Jack, after your week's toil?"

Jack shook his head. "I want to catch up with my reading. You take the skiff, Spider. But get back early. Low tide's at four-thirty."

"Sure," Spider said, but he didn't return until well after midnight, when the skiff, bumping the sloop, awakened Jack.

Coming below, Spider muttered, "Them waterfront places clean you out quick." He turned out his empty pockets. "Broke again." He flung himself into his bunk without taking off his clothes.

*   *   *

In pitch-black darkness, the *Razzle Dazzle* crept along the shore line. Not a star glimmered through the murky overcast and only the occasional flickering of a shoreside light served to guide the sloop.

"Nothin' to worry about," Spider said, yawning. "Worst that could happen would be to ground in the mud, and the incomin' tide would float us off." He yawned again. "You should've seen Young Scratch Nelson tossin' away his money last night. I'll bet he's still at it."

"Better take some soundings, Spider."

"Sure, if you say so." Spider took the hand-lead from the cockpit locker and went forward. Presently, he called out: "Mud bottom with some shell. No use takin' any more soundings, though." Returning aft, he pointed over the starboard bow. "Look over there. See them stakes?"

A row of stakes, driven into the bay bottom, could be seen in the pale light cast by the running lamps. "Them's to keep sting rays out of the beds. Sting rays eat oyster for breakfast, lunch, an' supper." He paused. "We can drop the mudhook anywhere 'round here and take the skiff in."

Two anchors were dropped to hold the sloop in the soft bottom. The canvas was hauled down and furled, and the skiff brought alongside. Spider, a bundle of gunny sacks under his arm, jumped down into the small craft. Jack, following with a lantern, asked, "Do you think we'll need so many sacks?"

"You never can tell when you're goin' to be lucky," Spider said. "Row up to the stakes and I'll spread 'em apart from the bow so's we can slide through."

Inside the stakes, Jack rowed until the skiff nudged the bottom. They both got out and their sea boots crunching in mud and shell, dragged the skiff up onto the tide flat.

The lantern shed a pale circle of light over what at first appeared to be a bed of empty shell. But upon stooping over, Jack soon found that many of the shells contained live oysters, a number of them large enough to be saleable.

"Say, Spider!" he exclaimed, "I think we've struck something good."

"It does look that way, don't it?" Spider muttered. "Well, let's get busy 'fore the tide chases us out."

The tide had already turned. Jack could hear it lapping the flats as he set to work, scraping the largest oysters from the bed. He began working feverishly and by the time dawn was breaking, he had filled three sacks to Spider's one.

Spider, looking at Jack's cut and bleeding

hands, grinned one-sidedly. "You went at it too fast," he said. "Anyhow, it bests dredgin', don't it?"

The tide was running in fast. They were able to float the skiff to the bulging sacks. Lifting them aboard, they rowed back out to the sloop.

"We certainly were lucky, Spider," Jack said. "We'll go back tomorrow morning. The tide will be low an hour later and that means more daylight. We'll do even better than we did today."

"Maybe," Spider said. "Maybe we will and maybe we won't."

Jack wondered about this strange remark, but Spider refused to answer any questions. It wasn't until the following morning that he found out what Spider meant.

As the *Razzle Dazzle* approached the shallow beds off Millbrae just before dawn that next morning, Jack was puzzled by the number of lights which gleamed dead ahead. "Red and green," he said to Spider. "Those are running lights. Looks as if someone is there ahead of us."

"Sure," Spider said. "You didn't figure we had them rich beds all to ourselves, did you? Nelson and Joe Goose an' the rest of the

pirates come here regular. They'd have been here yesterday if they hadn't been out all night, having a good time for themselves on the waterfront."

He gave Jack a sidewise look before he went on. "It wouldn't surprise me none if we run into trouble. Them fellas are pretty tough an' they don't like strangers on their territory."

"I see," Jack said quietly.

"Now's your chance to turn back," Spider muttered. "Remember, if you keep on goin', I ain't fightin' your battles."

"Stay on the course," Jack said. "We're going in. Stand by to drop the hook."

In the slow breaking dawn, the *Razzle Dazzle* nosed into an anchorage between two other sloops. About a half dozen craft were riding at anchor and several skiffs were pushing in through the stakes. Already, dark forms could be seen bent over on the tide flats.

When the sloop was secure, Jack said, "Stay aboard, Spider. Sing out if anybody tries to board her." He got into the skiff and Spider passed down the lantern and the sacks.

Jack rowed in through a gap in the stakes some other boat had made, and calmly began filling a sack. All around him the pirates were intently scooping up oysters.

They paid no attention to the boy, but he knew that was only because they had not recognized a stranger in the darkness. Sooner or later, they would notice that he wasn't one of their crew.

He had filled one sack and was starting on the second when a voice rang out: "Hey, you!" Jack looked up and saw a tall, black-bearded young man striding toward him.

"Get out," the man said. "Leave them oysters where they lay and get out of here before you get hurt."

Jack straightened and faced the stranger. "I've as much right here as you have. I'm staying."

"That's what you think." Blackbeard cupped his hands and shouted, "Hey, Scratch! Clam! Come over here. We got company."

Jack stood his ground as the others appeared. Young Scratch Nelson stood, hands on hips, grinning widely.

"I seen him around," Nelson said. "He's the bookworm Spider was tellin' us about. Bought *Razzle Dazzle* from French Frank. Take him on, Blacky." He turned to the thick-set youth swaggering beside him. "You stay out of it, Clam. One at a time. If he's lucky and gets both of you, then—" he rubbed his big red hands together, "I'll smash him."

Jack didn't wait. He leaped for Blacky, ducking under a wide, right-hand swing, and drove his right fist into the pirate's jaw. He followed with a left as Blacky reeled, and then a right which sent the man sprawling. Without hesitating, Jack sprang at the man called Clam, who hardly had time to get his fists up before Jack was on him.

Clam was tough. He pinned Jack's arms against his body. With a mighty effort, Jack broke free and rained blows on the man's face. A furious swing sent Jack to his knees, but a second later he was erect again, driving in. A right and a left—another right, and Clam went down muttering: "That's enough."

Breathing heavily, Jack turned to face Young Scratch Nelson who towered over him by nearly six inches. Young Scratch was grinning. "This—" he started to say.

Suddenly, a shot rang out, and his grin froze. "Cops!" he yelled. "Back to the boats." As he and Jack ran toward their skiffs, he shouted, "You're okay, kid. You're all right. I don't think anybody will be botherin' you after this."

Spider had the canvas up on the *Razzle Dazzle* by the time Jack scrambled aboard.

When the anchors came up and she sped out into the open water, Spider said, "I saw that fight. You sure can use your fists, Jack."

Jack looked squarely at his deckhand. "Spider, why didn't you tell me these shallow beds are privately owned?"

Spider chuckled. "I figured it would be a good joke on you when you tumbled to it. You're a true oyster pirate, now."

The Fish Patrol

⚓ MANY MONTHS LATER, JACK sat down beside Pete, the Italian fisherman, in front of the wharf shed.

"Look at that net," Pete said, shaking his head. "Those big sea lions, they get in when they're chasing the fish, and they tear it up just like it was made out of thread. Well, maybe I can fix it." He looked up from his task. "How you been, Jack? I hear you are partners with that wild fellow, Nelson."

Jack nodded. "Young Scratch and I joined forces after I lost the *Razzle Dazzle,*

Pete. He's wild, all right, be he's a good sailor."

"You're a good sailor, too," Pete said. "Jack, I never saw you look so fine. Your face is brown like a nut. You got good hard muscles. But—I think I see something unhappy in your eyes. Is that because you lose the *Razzle Dazzle?*"

"No, it isn't that, Pete," Jack said slowly. "Do you remember that day when French Frank tried to sell you the sloop?"

"Sure. It was almost a year ago, wasn't it?"

"You said something that day, Pete. I guess most of it went in one ear and out the other, but some of it stuck in my mind. You told me that making money too easily made a person weak and sick, deep inside."

"I remember. I still think that, Jack."

"It's a strange thing, Pete—" Jack paused. "You can drift into a way of life without really knowing it."

Pete chuckled. "I think, maybe, I know you better than you know yourself, Jack. I watch you. I see you sail in ahead of everybody to the wharf, always with the biggest load of oysters. You do something, you do it good, better than anybody. That's why you are the best oyster pirate in the business and make more money than any of the others."

"At first, Pete, everything looked fine," Jack said in a taut voice. "I made money. I paid back Jenny Prentiss. I gave my mother and father more money than they'd seen for many a day. But now—trouble has started."

The old man nodded. He had heard that the pirates had begun fighting among themselves. Some, like Clam and Blackie, were not satisfied with the profits from oyster piracy, and besides, they considered oystering hard work. They had taken to robbing the Chinese, Greek, and Italian fishermen of their catches on the upper bay. Others even raided shoreside chandlers' stores.

"You do something that isn't right and it isn't long before you do something very bad." Pete kept his eyes on his net.

"Young Scratch and I wanted no part of the things they did," Jack explained. "Spider deserted me to join Clam and the others. We split up into two gangs and then the fighting started."

Pete nodded. "I hear about how they sneak up at night and set fire to your sloop. Then I read in the newspaper that they are caught stealing a safe and now they are all in San

Quentin prison. I guess that made you think pretty hard, hey, Jack?"

"Yes, it did. But not hard enough to keep me from going in with Young Scratch in his *Reindeer*. So, I'm still an oyster pirate and— I don't like it. I'm off course, Pete. Why, I might even get to be like Clam and Blackie and end up behind bars. I've got to get away from that kind of life, before I find myself on the rocks."

Pete put his hand on Jack's shoulder. "You're a good boy, Jack. You will never drift on the rocks. I know that. You think you want to do this, or that, but you don't know for sure. Some day, you'll find out and then you will make a big success. I know."

Jack lowered his eyes. "I haven't been reading and studying as I planned. I'm not learning anything much — except how to break laws."

"Jack, maybe I can help you. Tomorrow morning, I will tell somebody I know to come and see you and that Young Scratch on the *Reindeer*. This man is my good friend, Charlie Le Grant. When he comes, you listen to him good. You promise?"

Jack spent the afternoon in the Oakland Public Library. When he left, he took several books which Miss Coolbrith had helped him select. He stopped by his sister's house for a visit with Eliza and Captain Shepard. Then, for the first time in weeks, he went home. Somehow, he did not want to spend the night aboard the *Reindeer*.

"Jack!" His mother's eyes lit up when she saw him. "You've come home to stay?"

"Well, not exactly, Ma. But I'll try to come more often after this." He pulled out all his money—coins and bills—and laid it onto the kitchen table. "It's all for you."

Flora London frowned at the money. "I know that the cannery wasn't good for you, son. But what you are doing now is—" She turned away. "I think it's even worse in some ways. Surely, there must be some other kind of work . . ."

"You're right," Jack said. "I'm not **going** to be an oyster pirate much longer."

"You really mean that?" She looked at him, lovingly.

"I mean it. You'll see. Will Pa be home for supper?"

"No. He's working at the Davies' ferry slip as a night watchman. It isn't hard work. But I don't think the long night hours are good for him.

That evening Jack lost himself in *The Adventures of Huckleberry Finn*. When she gave him the thick brown volume, Miss Coolbrith had said, "I am very sure you'll like this one, Jack. It is by a writer who lived across the bay, in San Francisco—Samuel L. Clemens, who writes under the name of Mark Twain."

Jack was excited by Huck's story. He couldn't put the book aside and it was well after midnight before he finished it. Turning out the lamp, he thought: "If only I could write like that!" He closed his eyes and hoped that, in his dreams, he would relive the adventures of Huck and Tom Sawyer, as they sailed down the Mississippi River on a raft.

Jack roused himself the next morning just in time to have breakfast with his father who had returned from his job at the ferry slip.

"Everything all right with you, son?" John London asked as he took his place at the table.

"No, it isn't." Jack sat down next to his father. "I've always been able to talk things over with you. I should have come home long before this, but—" After Jack explained, his father nodded understandingly.

"I've been looking forward to this moment,

son. It's been mighty hard for me to keep silent all these months, but—advice from me wouldn't have done any good until you were ready to listen. This happened to be one of those things you had to figure out for yourself. And now that you've decided to give up oystering, what are you planning to do next?"

"I don't know, Pa. I've thought of shipping out as deckhand in a deep-water vessel. I'd like to see some of the places I've read about. Sometimes I think I should follow the sea, study navigation. Maybe I could work up to be a ship's officer, even a captain."

Jack London put his head over to one side and stared at his son. "You have a restless look in your eye. You're growing up fast, and every man has to chart his own course. I'm not surprised to hear that your ambition is to go to sea. But I'm glad you're beginning to see oyster pirating for what it is."

The following morning Jack was aboard the *Reindeer* again with Young Scratch Nelson when a voice hailed: "Ahoy, the *Reindeer*."

A skiff came alongside and a stocky man in a blue shirt swung aboard.

The stranger said with a smile: "My name is Charlie Le Grant. I'm with the Fish Patrol."

"Fish Patrol!" Young Scratch bridled. "Look here, Mister, we aint—"

"It's all right, Scratch," Jack interrupted. "Pete sent him."

Charlie Le Grant nodded. "I'm not here to make an arrest. Pete was telling me about you boys. I think I have a proposition that might work out well for all of us."

"We're doing all right as it is," Young Scratch said. "We—"

"I promised Pete to listen to Mr. Le Grant's proposition, Scratch," Jack broke in. "Let's go below. I'll put on some coffee."

Jack set a steaming mug on the table.

Le Grant leaned forward and spoke to the boys in a quiet, friendly voice. "I suppose you know why the Fish Patrol was set up a few years back."

"Sure," Young Scratch broke in, "so's fellows like you could have good jobs keeping fishermen from making a decent living."

"Some folks look at it that way," Charlie Le Grant answered. "But let's have a look at the other side of the coin. Maybe both of you are too young to remember that, a few years back, a fisherman could go out and fill up his boat in no time at all. In a few hours he could catch all he could sell."

"That's right," Young Scratch admitted. "My pa used to tell me you could scoop up shad with a bucket. Now, shad are mighty scarce."

"It's like this," Charlie Le Grant said. "You can't have your cake and eat it, too. For instance, if you don't give the salmon a chance to get up the river from the ocean to lay their eggs, the day will come when there won't be any salmon. That's why we have a law against netting of salmon in spawning season from sundown Saturday until sunup, Monday."

"That's fair enough," Jack remarked. "No sense killing the goose that lays the golden eggs."

"Sure, a law like that is all right," Young Scratch admitted.

Jack refilled the coffee mugs. "I should think," he said, "that fishermen would be in favor of laws like that, Mr. Le Grant."

"Most of them are," Le Grant said. "But there are men who break the laws and then outsail the Fish Patrol."

"Say," Young Scratch threw out his massive chest, "I'd like to see 'em outsail me if I was in the Fish Patrol."

Charlie Le Grant drank some coffee. Putting down the mug, he grinned. "Some of the lawbreakers like Big Nick, the Greek, carry rifles and don't hesitate to use them, either."

Jack nodded, wondering what the Fish Patrolman was leading up to.

"Boys," Charlie Le Grant said, "how would you like to join the Fish Patrol and help us catch these lawbreakers?"

"Us?" Young Scratch looked doubtful. "You woudn't take us in, would you? A couple of oyster pirates—"

"You wouldn't be regular patrolmen," Le Grant explained. "You wouldn't be paid regular wages, but you'd have a chance to make money. If you work hard enough, you might make more than a patrolman like myself."

"How's that?" Young Scratch asked.

"Here's how it works. You'd be deputy patrolmen, sailing your own sloop. You'd get paid so much for her charter, and as deputies, you would share in the fines paid by lawbreakers you help catch. The way you boys can sail, you ought to do right well for yourselves. What do you say?"

Jack's heart pounded. Le Grant's proposition suited him well. He could still live on the water, but he would be on the right side of the law. "I'm all for it," he said. "But Scratch owns the *Reindeer*." He looked across at his partner sprawled on the opposite bench.

"I'm on," Young Scratch Nelson said. "For a while, anyway. Show us where this Big Nick hides out. We'll bring him in for you."

* * *

During the next few months, the *Reindeer* sailed in the northern waters of the great harbor. She ran up past San Quentin Point where the grim walls of the state prison shouldered up from the beach. She passed San Rafael, up through San Pablo Straits into the wide expanse of San Pablo Bay.

Jack, Young Scratch, and Charlie Le Grant boarded vessel after vessel, making many arrests. After that, they sailed up through the swift running narrows of Carquinez Straits. Here, where the San Joaquin and Sacramento rivers join forces to sweep through to the bay, they took after the shad fishermen who ignored the law.

As time went on, Young Scratch became increasingly restless. "This is mighty tame work, Jack," he said, one day, as the sloop nosed through a thick fog off Benicia. "I figured it would be more exciting. Besides, we ain't seen hide or hair of this Big Nick."

It was plain that Young Scratch had begun

to miss his wild friends along the Oakland waterfront. Jack realized that, before long, the Fish Patrol would lose the *Reindeer* and he would lose his job. "But," he said to Charlie Le Grant, "maybe it's just as well. Somehow, this isn't the kind of work I want to do all my life."

"You want to go to sea, don't you?" Charlie asked.

Jack hesitated before replying, "I think I'd like to become a ship's officer."

Charlie Le Grant nodded thoughtfully. "Could be, you just want to see some of those places you've been reading about."

"Could be," Jack admitted with a smile.

"Well," Le Grant said slowly, "I hope I won't lose you boys too soon. The salmon run is just about to start."

"I think Scratch will stay on for that," Jack said, his smile deepening. "He wants to have a chance at Big Nick."

Jack and his partner had their first glimpse of Big Nick on the wharf at Benicia. It was late August and the big fall salmon run was beginning. Boats dotted the waters of San Pablo Bay and Carquinez Strait. Hundreds of nets had been spread across the channels. And the big king salmon came surging in.

"Funny thing," Charlie Le Grant said. "Seems like nothing can stop a salmon in spawning season except, maybe, a net. Why, I've seen 'em wiggle through shallows a goldfish couldn't live in. No current is too swift for 'em and hardly a waterfall too high for 'em to leap. They find a spot in some stream, scoop out a hole and lay their eggs, and cover 'em up. Then, they die." He broke off as a trim-looking salmon boat with a great spread of canvas came in toward the wharf. "There he is! That's Big Nick, boys."

For a moment, Jack thought the vessel would crash into the pilings. Then, suddenly, it went into a series of short tacks.

"He's seen us," the patrolman said as the boat scudded through the crowded shipping. "Look at him show off."

"He can handle that boat, all right," Young Scratch muttered.

"Think you could catch him?" asked Charlie Le Grant.

Young Scratch's eyes narrowed. "Give me enough wind and I'll catch anything that floats in this bay."

The salmon boat slid neatly alongside the wharf just astern of the *Reindeer*. His lines fast and canvas furled, Big Nick stepped onto the wharf, grinning down from his six-and-a-half-foot height. "So," he bellowed, "it is my old friend, Charlie Le Grant. Come to catch Big Nick, eh? Well, you get a chance. To-morrow is Sunday and I go fishing, law or no law."

"He's pretty sure of himself," Jack commented, as the man swaggered off.

"Why not? Nobody's caught him yet. Besides, if anyone gets too close to him, he brings out his rifle. Care to tackle him in the morning, boys?"

"We'll tackle him, all right," Young Scratch said grimly.

True to his boast, the huge fisherman was on the water at dawn. From the wharf, through the glass, they could see him hauling the big salmon into his boat.

But they didn't catch him. What little wind blew seemed just right for Big Nick. Before the *Reindeer* got near him, his nets were in and he was off on a long tack for the opposite shore. The sloop gave chase, but the smaller craft was faster and could sail closer to the wind.

The same thing happened the following weekend. But, on the third Sunday, Young Scratch grinned broadly as he saw the straits churning into whitecaps, before a stiff north-easterly. "Let's go!"

"Better reef the mains'l, hadn't we?" Charlie Le Grant said. "Man, she's blowing."

"Reef?" Young Scratch laughed. "We never reef."

Big Nick, seeing the sloop get underway, hauled in his nets and streaked off. The *Reindeer*, every inch of canvas aloft, tore after him. The sloop leaned against the wind until her topside was almost under and it was all the patrolman could do to keep her bailed out.

"You'll blow the sticks out of her," he yelled, and Jack grinned. He and Scratch had been through worse than this.

Bobbing in the swells and fighting the tide and current, Big Nick's little craft was no match for the *Reindeer*. The Greek fisherman ducked and dodged, but always the sloop came around, cutting him off and drawing closer.

"Look out," Charlie Le Grant shouted. "He's going to shoot!"

A shot came downwind and the bullet whined past Jack's ear.

"He won't do much more shootin'," cried Young Scratch from the tiller. "Not unless he's got three hands. Look, he's in trouble already!"

The smaller boat was almost on her beam ends as the *Reindeer* bore down. Big Nick's mainsail crumpled and she righted herself as the sloop drew nearer.

The patrolman shouted: "Scratch, bring her alongside. I'm going aboard."

Seconds later, he leaped for the deck of the disabled salmon boat, covering the fisherman with his pistol. Soon Big Nick was aboard the sloop, bound hand and foot. His own boat was towing behind the *Reindeer* as they stood in for Benicia.

"Well, Jack," Young Scratch said when Charlie Le Grant took Big Nick off to prison, "I guess it's about time for me to say good-by to the Fish Patrol. Why, I ain't had a good fight since I've been in it."

"You miss that kind of thing, Scratch?" Jack asked.

"Yes, I sure do," Young Scratch said. "Somehow, breakin' the law's more fun than enforcin' it. Anyway, I'm off to Oakland to-night." He looked at Jack. "What're you figurin' on doin'?"

"I think I'll try to sign on one of the sealing schooners out of San Francisco," Jack said, slowly.

"What's the matter, Jack. Ain't Frisco Bay big enough for you?"

Jack grinned. He suddenly felt very good. With a surge of energy it seemed that the whole world wasn't too big to tackle. And all he'd seen so far was San Francisco Bay. It was like his father had said, a man has to chart his own course. How could you tell, until you'd ventured, where you'd find the thing you were looking for?

He stared across the water at the distant spires and hills of San Francisco, and then at the boats bobbing up and down in the waters of the Estuary, and almost forgot to answer Scratch Nelson's question.

"Big enough?" he muttered, more to himself than to his friend. "It doesn't seem to be."

In Search of the Seal Herd

HEAVY MORNING FOG blanketed the bay as the ferryboat *Oakland* churned toward San Francisco. Her fog whistle bleated and Jack London, standing in the bow, listened to the answering voices from the gray mist. Now and again he saw the ghostly shape of some other craft slipping past.

Soon the spire of the Ferry Building loomed ahead. A bell rang below and the ferry's engines were silenced. She slid gently into the yawning arms of the slip.

As he hurried ashore, Jack thought of what Charlie Le Grant had said: "Jack, I don't like to see you leave us. You could become a regular patrolman if you wanted to stay, but—" He shrugged. "I don't know what you're after and I guess you don't know either. I've seen you searching for it in the books. Now, maybe, you figure it's somewhere over the horizon. Anyway, since you're bound and determined to go to sea . . ."

The patrolman had scribbled a couple of lines on a slip of paper: *Joe Harris, Marine Outfitter, Sacramento Street, San Francisco.*

"Joe's a friend of mine," Le Grant had said, as he handed Jack the paper. "There's not much going on along the Frisco waterfront that Joe isn't on to. He'll see that you get a decent berth in one of the sealers."

Jack set out now to find the marine outfitter. He threaded his way past the horse-drawn street cars, drays, and buggies, on East Street, and turned into lower Sacramento Street. Under a canvas awning, which dripped with fog, was a sign, lettered in gold:

THE JOE HARRIS CO.

Jack went inside and paused in front of a glass-enclosed counter which contained boatswain's whistles, sheathe-knives, watches, and hand-compasses. He was looking at these intently when a pleasant voice said: "And what can I do for you, young man?"

Jack looked up to see a smiling, alert-looking, young man behind the counter. "My name is Jack London, and—" He mentioned Charlie Le Grant and then explained that he wanted to ship out as a seaman in one of the sealers.

"A friend of Charlie's is a friend of mine. I'm Joe Harris." He extended his hand. "How old are you, Jack?"

"Nearly seventeen, sir."

Joe Harris nodded. "There are berths to be had, but most of them are aboard vessels no sailor in his right mind would ship in. It takes knockout drops to provide crews for some of the hard-case skippers and mates who sail out of this port. Belaying-pin soup and handspike hash make up most of the bill-of-fare aboard those packets."

He rubbed his chin thoughtfully. "Here's what I'll do, Jack. I'll talk to some of the lads I know in the sealing fleet. Drop back this afternoon and possibly, I'll have some good news for you."

With time on his hands, Jack decided to explore the city, where he had been born.

His family had moved to Oakland when he was less than a year old and during his boyhood he'd only crossed the bay to visit the city a few times. He felt almost a stranger as he walked northward on East Street.

The street twisted and curved along the lip of the bay. It seemed hardly a street at all, this muddy road, edged here and there, with a rough boardwalk.

But the long wharves on pilings nosed out into the bay and, as Jack walked slowly along, the sun broke through the fog and shone on a crowd of brigantines, schooners and full-rigged ships. There were steamboats, too—the Pacific Mail and Oceanic lines.

Jack sniffed the tangy smells of spices and tar. This was the scent of adventure! And there was the sound of adventure, too—the foreign tongues he heard, as he walked beside Chinese, Hindus, and Malayans.

Turning west, Jack came to a district of sailors' boarding houses and inns: *The Red Rooster* and the *Melodeon* and the *Bella Union*. He knew he was in the Barbary Coast. But the streets, the scene of so many wild tales, were deserted. It was as if the Barbary Coast was deep in sleep.

On to Montgomery Street, where he saw the

well-dressed businessmen and fashionably gowned ladies in their fine carriages. At Clay Street, he watched a cable car climb the hill like a fly walking up a wall.

He toiled up afoot, wanting a close look at the mansions on top of the hill. He would have liked a ride on the curious contraption, but he had other uses for his pennies.

Staring at the stately houses, he thought of the books they must hold. People who lived in mansions could buy all the books they wanted.

He turned down California Street and found a bookstore. For nearly two hours he fingered the secondhand volumes in the stalls on the sidewalk. He saw dozens of books he'd have liked to own and finally chose two well-worn books—a dictionary and an account of travels in Japan. They cost him a nickle apiece.

It was mid-afternoon when he returned to the waterfront. He found Joe Harris talking with a stocky, sun-bronzed man.

"Come over here, Jack," Mr. Harris called. "I want you to meet Pete Holt. Pete is a seal hunter on the *Sophie Sutherland*. Pete, this is Jack London, the lad I was telling you about."

Jack felt his hand gripped by fingers that

were all muscle. "So," Pete Holt said, "you want to ship in a sealer? Had much experience with small boats?"

"Yes, sir." Jack told the seal hunter about his oystering and his work with the Fish Patrol. "Of course," he added, "I've never been out of San Francisco harbor."

Pete Holt chuckled. "The ocean's a bit larger than the bay, but—I figure you'll do. On the sealing grounds, you'll pull an oar or man a sail in one of the small boats. For the rest of the voyage, you'll be an able seaman. How does that sound?"

"It sounds fine," Jack replied.

"All right, then," Holt said. "Joe, here, will fix you up with sea bag, oilskins, and anything else you need. We sign articles at nine tomorrow morning. Be on time, Jack."

*   *   *

Late the next afternoon, the sealing schooner *Sophie Sutherland* slipped out the Golden Gate. Plunging into the open sea, her bow flung up sheets of spray as she met the long Pacific swells. The setting sun glowed red on her great expanse of canvas as she steadied to the wind.

The *Sophie* was running southwesterly. At the Bonin Islands, five thousand miles away, she would meet up with the rest of the sealing fleet.

Jack, clearing the deck of gear, glanced up as the swift schooner left the California coast astern. He remembered his mother's tears and his father's quiet: "Good luck, son." There had not been much time for farewells. He'd stayed longer than he had intended at the Oakland Public Library, where Miss Coolbrith had given him an armful of books from her own collection, to take on the voyage.

When supper was called, Jack joined the line to the galley, just aft of the foremast. The sea cook, wearing a gunny sack for an apron, filled the men's plates with stew and their tin cups with tea. Jack followed his shipmates down through a hatchway to the forecastle for his first meal at sea.

Most of the seamen in his watch were Scandinavians. They were seasoned, deepwater sailors and Jack had the feeling of being an outsider. In their eyes, he was a grass-green sailor, young and inexperienced. As they sat around on their sea chests and bunks, talking while they ate, Jack listened quietly.

The oil lamp swung to the schooner's motion, casting crazy shadows. The sound of the sea pounding the bows thundered as the men spoke of far-off ports. They ignored Jack for the most part and yarned about other ships, about cranky mates and hard-case skippers.

There was grumbling too; grumbling about the grub, the work, the officers, and the ship generally. One of the sailors, a wide-shouldered Swede the men called Red John, seemed to be doing most of the complaining.

"Now," he said loudly, waving his fork, "just take them hunters. Six of 'em, we got aboard. They sleep in the cabin aft, hard by the skipper an' mate. They eat with the officers, with a cabin boy to wait on 'em hand an' foot. An' they don't do a lick of work, just sit around all day while we—"

"Pipe down," a young Norwegian, named Axel, broke in. "They pick out those hunters because they're crack shots. You'd give your right eye to be a hunter yourself."

"I can shoot seals as good as they do," Red John shouted. "Those hunters are worthless ballast, I tell you, just like—" He turned and scowled squarely at Jack. "Just like him."

Jack felt all eyes on him, but he said nothing.

"Let him alone, John," Axel said. "He hasn't had a chance to get his sea legs yet. Give him time."

"While the rest of us do his work, eh? So he can lay in his bunk readin' books?"

"Books?" somebody growled. "He's got books?"

Red John pointed to Jack's canvas sea bag. "I saw 'em when he was gettin' out his oil-skins. He's got that bag crammed with books. I guess he thinks he's better'n we are with his book learnin'." He rose and stood above Jack and muttered, "Maybe I can teach you something what ain't in books."

The young Norwegian and another sailor grasped the big Swede's arms. "Give the kid a chance to learn the ropes, John," Axel said.

Red John, still muttering about worthless ballast, piped down, but Jack knew that there were breakers ahead.

In the meantime, he set himself to the task of making good at the job. Whenever the watch was called, Jack was the first on deck, ready to do his full share of the work, no matter how hard it might be or how dangerous.

The *Sophie Sutherland*, giant ship that she was, handled pretty much like the *Razzle Dazzle*. Like his own lost sloop, she was fore and aft rigged. She was ninety feet in length with a twenty-three foot beam, and her main mast reached up a hundred feet from the deck. She carried two spars instead of one; a foremast and main. Also, she carried topsails. Yet her canvas was controlled in much the same manner as the smaller boat.

Before very many days had passed, Jack was at home in the schooner, on deck or aloft. He could handle a wheel-watch and box the compass. He could match anyone climbing up to set or take in the upper sails, or shift the topsail sheets and tacks. All the men aboard —except Red John—agreed that Jack London was holding up his end—and more.

The sulky Swede baited Jack at every opportunity. Jack realized this could not go on much longer. Some day, something was bound to happen.

It happened twelve days out of San Francisco during Jack's watch below. While his shipmates sat around, weaving rope-yarn mats or mending their clothes, Jack was deep in a book. Now and again, he would put down Herman Melville's great whaling story, *Moby Dick,* and open his dictionary to look up the meaning of a word he did not understand.

Heavy footsteps thumped down the companionway, and Red John entered the forecastle. He stood, hands on hips, glaring down at Jack, but the boy kept his eyes on the printed page.

"Hey, you, lubber," Red John grunted, "put down them books. I got work for you. You start right now and you swab out this forecastle. You hear?"

"Say—" Louis, a fellow-Swede, looked up from mending a shirt. "What're you trying to pull, anyway? This happens to be your peggy-day, John."

"I don't care whose peggy-day it is," Red John roared. "I give greeny an order and he jumps, or by jiminy, I make him jump." With one hand, he knocked the books from Jack's bunk. With the other he smacked the boy squarely in the face.

Jack leaped to his feet. Red John was twice his size, but that made no difference. The time had come for a showdown—a fight. Calling on all the rough and tumble tricks he'd learned during his days with the oyster pirates, Jack went into action. He darted in, hammering at the big man with his fists. Ducking under the other's huge arms, he leaped onto the broad back.

Bellowing with rage, Red John tried to shake Jack off. He swung around, slamming the boy against the deck beams, but Jack

would not let go. He tightened his leg grip, hammered the big man's head with his fists until Red John, half-blinded and nearly strangled, gasped: "I got enough. Let go."

Louis, Axel, and the others were laughing uproariously. Jack half expected Red John would be in a rage.

Instead, the Swede rubbed his neck and said: "You caught me good with that trick, but—that's all right. You defend yourself." He thrust out a huge paw. "Shake hands, Jack." He grinned widely. "You and me are friends now."

Thereafter, nobody bothered Jack. On his watches below, he read and studied, using for light a shaded oil lamp he had made himself.

It was flying fish weather all the way to the Bonin Islands. Here, southeast of Japan, where the sealing fleet put in for water and supplies, Jack stepped onto foreign soil for the first time. He wandered about the coral beach and the settlement. The Japanese houses looked so frail that he didn't see how they could stand up. Yet for all their frailty he saw them weather a gale. He ate strange foods, listened to foreign talk, and sucked it all in like a thirsty man getting his first drink at a spring.

The rest of the sealing fleet was already in the harbor and, all too soon, the *Sophie Sutherland's* anchor was hauled up from the coral bottom. Her sails filled and she was off once more, northbound for the coast of Siberia to find the seal-herd rookeries in the Bering Sea.

Typhoon

❧ THE LOOKOUT SHOUTED AND Jack, running to the starboard rail, saw the seals. There were thousands of them, their heads bobbing in the bleak gray sea. Nobody could tell the boy where they came from. It was known only that they would appear in these waters in the spring, after wintering somewhere in the southern seas. The sealers weren't curious. All they cared about was getting as many as possible while the herd was swimming northward.

An order lifted from aft. The *Sophie Sutherland*'s six boats were manned by a hunter, a boatpuller, and a steerer. They were unlashed and lowered, and fanned out as they approached the edge of the rookery.

Pete Holt sat in the bow of Jack's boat holding a rifle across his knees. "Quiet," he cautioned. "Seals scare easy."

With the oars and oarlocks bound with leather and rope yarn, the boats crept up silently upon the unsuspecting herd. Before long the first boat was among the seals. Jack heard the sound of a shot.

That was the beginning. As the other boats moved in, the reports of the hunters' guns echoed across a sea which became stained red with blood. Jack and his boat-steerer had plenty to do. Not only did they have to manage the boat in the heavy swells, but they had to get lines on the dead seals and secure them alongside, until the schooner ran up and hauled them aboard.

To Jack, seal-hunting was a nightmare—a nightmare which lasted for three months in the bleak wind-whipped, fogbound, northern seas. He hated the killing of these helpless creatures, and he was shocked by the waste. Hardly one seal in five was taken after having been shot. Some sank; others, wounded, escaped, only to die in the depths of the ocean.

The *Sophie Sutherland* followed the herd up along the Siberian coast and into the Bering Sea. Much as Jack hated the work, he managed the sealing boat skillfully. Pete Holt, his hunter, could depend on him. Aboard ship, the task of skinning the animals, heaving the carcasses over the side to the waiting sharks, and salting down the skins, was as distasteful as the hunt.

Jack was glad when it was over—when the last seal skin was in the hold, the decks swabbed clean, and the *Sophie Sutherland's* prow turned southward toward Japan. At Yokohama she would take on water and supplies, then sail for home.

*   *   *

The schooner was nearing the Japanese coast when Red John came into the forecastle. "I smell weather," he announced. "She's goin' to blow come tomorrow."

Jack looked up from his book. "Well, we're used to it. We saw some mighty rough seas up north."

Red John laughed shortly. "You call that weather?" He snorted. "You wait!"

When, the next day, the sun rose in a brilliant scarlet dawn, Jack was reminded of the old saying: "A red sky in the morning is the sailor's warning." A light breeze came out of the west, but within a few hours it was gone. The schooner rocked gently in the calm, her canvas drooping lifelessly.

As the crew ate their midday meal on the foredeck, Red John gazed out at the glassy sea. Sniffing, he muttered, "She's acomin'. I tell you, she's acomin'."

Aft, Jack saw the officers pacing back and forth as they watched the sky. By four bells, a dark ribbon of cloud appeared on the eastern horizon, rising slowly until it took the shape of a black, billowing tent. The heat was almost unbearable. Nerves were taut.

Jack couldn't keep his eyes off the cloud. It rose higher and higher, hovering in the eastern sky like a huge bat. Little gusts of wind caught at the canvas and orders came to take in the topsails and secure the vessel for heavy weather. Extra lashings were bent on the small boats and deck gear. Oil bags and a sea anchor were made ready.

The sun became a pale coin in the blackened sky. Whitecaps began flecking the sea. By nightfall, the *Sophie Sutherland*, stripped to storm canvas, was hove-to on the starboard tack in a howling gale. Pitching and rolling, she met the oncoming seas, creaking and groaning in every timber.

It was Jack's watch below. His shipmates usually turned into their bunks as soon as supper was over. But tonight they sat around, strangely silent, as if they were waiting for something.

For what, he wondered? Surely, the weather couldn't get any worse. He was about to voice the thought when the schooner was struck a hammer blow and she lurched crazily. Jack was sent sprawling across the forecastle.

As he rose, a voice bellowed down: "All hands. All hands on deck."

Jack clawed his way up the companionway after his mates. It was all he could do to remain erect. But, finally, he reached the deck —and the screaming gale. He was trying to get his bearings in the blackness when a giant sea thundered aboard and pitched him against the bulwarks.

Blindly his fingers found something to cling to, as the surging water dragged at him. He felt his grip giving way and the terrifying thought flashed into his mind that he was about to be washed overboard.

For endless seconds he fought the pull of

the sea. Then, suddenly, he knew he had won out. Choking, he rose and made his way aft. There was work to be done if the schooner was to be saved.

He saw the next wave before it broke on deck and he leaped for the ropes, hanging on until it passed. It can't get any worse, he thought. But it did. The sealer was like a crazed creature, twisting, leaping, and rolling. A hundred times during the night Jack wondered why she did not turn over on her beam ends. But, always, she came back to face the next blow. And all during this time, the crew manned the pumps or worked at clearing away broken spars and smashed gear.

Sometime during the night a patch of clear, starry sky appeared overhead.

"It's over," Jack panted.

"No," Red John growled. "It's just that we've hit the middle of it. The storm's eye. Soon, the wind will come a-howlin' from the opposite direction. That's the way of a typhoon."

Jack looked up. The patch of clear sky was gone. The wind came howling out of the west, driving the mountainous seas. The fight to stay alive went on through the night.

At dawn the gale lost its force and the *Sophie*

Sutherland tossed in the gray, tumbling seas. Four of the sealing boats had disappeared, ripped clear of their double lashings and driven overboard. Breaks had appeared in the bulwarks, and tangled wreckage cluttered the decks. Where the cook's galley had been there was now only the iron stove, half adrift.

Jack ached with weariness, yet he felt a glowing satisfaction and a tingling pride when Red John put a hand on his shoulder. "You're all right, Jack," the big man bellowed. "You're a real deepwater sailor, now."

A real deepwater sailor, Jack thought, straightening his tired shoulders. That was something a man could be proud of being and, for the first time, he fully understood why it was so. To meet the challenge of the sea forthrightly— He nodded to himself.

He wrote his father while the *Sophie Sutherland* was in Yokohama for repairs. *"First, the wind came howling out of the east and—"*

* * *

During the long voyage home, Jack listened to his shipmates making plans for the future. They all knew exactly what they were going to do when they were paid off:—No more throwing away their hard-earned money along the waterfront. No more getting into the clutches of boardinghouse runners.

"I'm staying away from the Barbary Coast like I would from sharks," Louis said. "And I'm not going to ship out in any more sealers. I've got my eye on a little chicken ranch over by Hayward. That's the life for a man. Just gather up the eggs every day and rake in the coin."

Axel had another idea: "I'm going to study up on navigation and get my third mate's papers."

Red John was going to make a long visit home. He was going back to Sweden and the old folks. He hadn't seen them since he'd run away to sea many years before.

Jack frowned uncertainly. If only it were possible to find a job which would pay enough so that he could not only help his family but have time to study! The years were slipping by so quickly and a high school education seemed as far off as ever. Yet, unless, he had that, college was out of the question.

"I don't know what I'm going to do," he muttered.

The *Sophie Sutherland* passed the Farralone Islands and the Golden Gate. She ran in through the straits and anchored off shore, while the port doctors came aboard. Before they pulled into the dock, Jack saw the little boats of the boardinghouse runners alongside the ship. The runners called out the names of the boardinghouse and praised the comforts offered.

"Stand off, y'scum," Red John shouted. "Come aboard, and I'll crack your heads together like walnuts."

The runners sheered off, but, thick as flies, they were on the wharf when the *Sophie Sutherland* tied up. Later, when the crew was paid off, the runners were at hand again urging the seamen to put up at one boardinghouse or another.

Red John, jingling the money in his pockets, turned toward his mates. With a sudden grin, he cried, "Come on, all of you! Just a little celebration before I shove off to Sweden."

Jack watched the crew fall in behind Red John, who led the way to a nearby inn. After a brief hesitation, Axel and Louis joined the rest.

Sea bag slung over his shoulder, Jack turned southward toward the Ferry Building. He knew what would happen to the *Sophie's* crew. The little celebration would grow into a big one. Before the men knew it, they would be in the hands of the boardinghouse runners, who would get the last of their pay.

The runners knew it, too. Looking back over his shoulder, Jack saw them waiting outside the inn. Red John would never see Sweden. Louis' chicken ranch was a hopeless dream. Axel would not study navigation. When their money ran out, they'd be carted off and delivered to an outgoing vessel in need of a crew.

Jack felt sorry for them. He knew that they wanted to forget the long months of drudgery at sea and this was the quickest, easiest way for them to do so. It wouldn't be hard, he realized, to slip into their kind of life — one in which no dreams could ever come true.

The Contest

⚓ TWO MONTHS LATER, TRUDG-
ing home along Oakland's darkening streets,
Jack wondered bitterly whether he was any
better off than those seamen. They'd been
tricked into signing up for another long and
dangerous voyage, all their bright plans behind
them. But his own hopes for the future were
smashed, too.

While he was off at sea a business panic
had swept the country with all the force of
a typhoon. He returned to find factories
closed and thousands of men out of work.
When he saw workmen wandering the streets

in Oakland, and San Francisco, or lined up at the soup kitchens, he thought he'd have to go back to oyster poaching.

A talk with Pete, the Italian fisherman, had put that idea out of his head.

"Those oyster pirates!" Pete had exclaimed. "Just like I say to you a long time ago—the easy money was no good for them. All of them get into trouble. French Frank is hiding up the river, but one of these days, the police will catch him and—he will hang. All those others—like Spider—are behind the bars in prison. And the crazy one who was your partner—he is dead."

"Dead?" Young Scratch Nelson dead? Jack could hardly believe it. "What happened to Scratch, Pete?"

"He robbed somebody. Then the police came and he ran away. So they shoot him." Pete shook his head.

With oyster pirating out, Jack had grabbed the first job that had offered itself—a place in the jute mill, weaving gunny sacks. The monotonous, unskilled toil from sunup to sundown paid just ten cents an hour, and the work left no time or energy for study. He had not read a book since he'd put foot on land.

"I can't go on at the jute mill," he decided, as he came within sight of his home.

"Why don't you become skilled in some trade, Jack?" his mother said, when the boy spoke of his decision.

But what trade? Should he become a bricklayer? A housepainter? Even the best of these craftsmen were out of work.

"Electricity?" Flora London suggested.

The mysterious energy that flowed through wires and made possible the telegraph and Edison's electric light stirred the boy's imagination. This was a wide open field. He sat erect, eyes glowing.

Then he shrugged. Special schooling would be needed and special schools cost money. To do anything with electricity was as impossible as going to high school or college. He went back next day, gloomier than ever, to the monotony of the jute mill.

A few nights later his father looked up from his newspaper. "There's one man who is going to do something about this panic," he said.

"What could one man do?" Jack asked.

"You can't tell. The *Call* has a long piece about this Jacob Coxey. Seems he's a rich man himself—owns a stone quarry somewhere in Ohio. He thinks the government could find useful jobs for the men out of work. Building roads and schools and such like. He wants all the unemployed to join in a march on Washington."

Jack's eyes lit up. Coxey offered action. He'd march with a leader like that.

"He'd have the government pay for the work with especially printed greenbacks," John London read on. "Thousands of unemployed men are joining up in Coxey's Army. There's talk about other armies forming in other cities."

"If one should start in Oakland or San Francisco," Jack said, "I'd join it."

"Now, Jack—" His mother came in from the kitchen and shook her head anxiously. "You're simply looking for an excuse to go off adventuring. Why, you're hardly back from Japan and already you're thinking of joining a lot of—hoboes. Don't you know that . . ."

Jack interrupted with a grin: "I know. A rolling stone gathers no moss. Well, I'm not gathering much moss at the jute mill."

"I can show you how to gather a little." Flora London turned toward her husband. "John, let me have that newspaper a minute."

She turned the page and said, "Here it is. It's an announcement of a writing contest for young people."

Jack stared at the announcement. "Cash prizes," he read aloud. "First award, twenty-five dollars."

"I've been thinking about that letter you sent us from Japan," his mother said eagerly. "It was a wonderful description of a typhoon. Of course, your letter isn't long enough for the contest. According to the rules, the article should be about two thousand words long. But you could add a few more words, couldn't you?"

"I—I don't know, Ma."

"Well, you could give it a try," John London challenged. "After all, twenty-five dollars isn't to be sneezed at."

Jack recalled the screaming gale and the thundering seas. The sounds and the terror were as clear in his mind as if he were still aboard the *Sophie Sutherland*. Suddenly he said, "I think I can do it."

"Fine, son," his father said. "You can start working on it Sunday."

"I'm starting right now," Jack said.

"Oh, no!" his mother said. "You're going to eat your supper first."

Jack pushed his plate away and dashed off to his room, sitting down at the little table where he kept his books and study notes. Dipping his pen, he wrote on ruled paper:

STORY OF A TYPHOON
OFF THE COAST OF JAPAN
by
JACK LONDON, *age 17*
It was four bells on the morning watch—

He wrote feverishly, reliving the roaring fury of the storm at sea. The pile of pages mounted as he described the storm he had witnessed from its beginning as a black ribbon of cloud on the horizon. He didn't stop until his mother called out that it was after midnight, that he'd have to get some sleep.

The next night, he was at it again. On the third night, he finished the article and counted the words. The rules called for two thousand — and he had written more than twice as many.

Painstakingly, he crossed out words and sentences, recopied the pages, and then read it over. When he was finished, he slumped back in his chair. He thought: It's no good. No

good at all. I won't send it in. The editor will laugh at those clumsy sentences.

Discouraged, Jack tossed the manuscript aside and went to bed.

In the bleak, depressing days that followed, Jack worked at the jute mill and tried to forget the award. He knew that his mother had made a special trip to San Francisco to deliver his manuscript to the editor of the *Call*. However, he was certain he wouldn't win anything. He told himself he should have known better than to even try to compete with the university students who knew all about the rules of writing and grammar.

Two weeks later, coming home from work one evening, Jack found his mother beaming, and his father smiling mysteriously.

"There's something in tonight's paper that might interest you, son," John London said, and he slowly unfolded the *Call*. "It seems that they've printed the names of the winners in that writing contest and—"

"Oh, tell him, John!" Mrs. London exclaimed.

"You won, son," John London said quietly.

"I—I won?" Jack's eyes widened. "Which prize?"

"First prize. Here, see for yourself." His father passed the newspaper over.

Jack London, aged 17, of Oakland, first prize winner. For his story of a typhoon off the coast of Japan—

The judges had been impressed. They said his work showed talent. Second and third prizes had been awarded to students at the University of California and Stanford.

Jack saw that the newspaper had printed the account of the typhoon, word for word, just as he had written it. As he read it, he wondered why it seemed so much better in print than in his handwriting. He could hardly believe these words were his.

He heard his mother say, "Just think of all the people who must be reading your article . . ."

Pride of achievement flooded through him warmly as he listened to his mother and father. And then, suddenly, an exciting thought flashed into his mind: I have found my trade—the writing trade. I'll get paid, not for what I do with my hands, but for what is in my head.

Twenty-five dollars for two thousand words! More than a cent a word. Why, he could earn a fine living at that rate. Already, other stories were taking shape in his mind. This very night, he'd write about the Bering Sea, the Bonin Islands, and Japan. He'd be able to write page after page and, at a cent a word, the jute mill could go hang.

Wonderful hours followed in the wake of the prize he had won. "I'm so proud of you, Jack," Jenny Prentiss had cried. And Eliza's husband, Captain Shepard said, "Stick with it, Jack. It isn't everyone who can put words on paper and make them come alive as you do."

And then there was the afternoon when Jack went to the Oakland Public Library. He wondered if Miss Coolbrith had seen his article in the *Call*. He longed to ask her but he probably wouldn't have the courage.

As Jack approached the librarian's desk, she smiled. "Jack," she said warmly, "I actually felt as though I were living through that terrible storm. You have real talent. You must go on with your writing."

"That's what I want to do, Miss Coolbrith. I want to be a writer more than anything else in the world. Since I won the prize, I've written more stories and have sent them to the newspapers. As soon as I get the money for them, I'm going to quit my job and write for a living."

"I hope you can do that." Miss Coolbrith looked at him thoughtfully. "But you mustn't be too impatient. A writer, especially in the beginning, often meets with disappointment. It isn't an easy life, Jack."

The boy smiled. He wasn't afraid of work. All he had to do was crowd on all canvas and make port.

"By the way," Miss Coolbrith said, "there's someone here who would like to meet you." She glanced toward a man who was browsing through the books on one of the shelves.

It seemed to Jack that there was something familiar about the stranger who came toward Miss Coolbrith's desk. A gentle smile played over his fine features. He wore a neat, well-pressed suit that made Jack remember uncomfortably that he had on work clothes, and shabby ones at that.

"George," Miss Coolbrith was saying, "this is Jack London whom you were asking about. Jack, this is George Sterling."

George Sterling! Now Jack knew why this man with the black curly hair had looked so familiar. The famous San Francisco's poet's picture appeared often in newspapers and magazines.

Jack was over-awed at meeting the poet. He felt panicky when Miss Coolbrith turned back to her desk and left them alone.

Sterling, however, proved easy to talk to. They discussed books for a while and then he spoke about Jack's prize-winning story.

"A remarkable piece of work for a beginner." he said. "Refreshingly honest. That's the way I'd like to be able to write, but—" and he smiled, "to do so, I expect I'd have to go through a typhoon and I shouldn't particularly like that. Tell me, do you intend to go on with your writing?"

"I certainly do," Jack replied. He told the poet about the other stories he had mailed to the newspapers and how he hoped to make a living from his pen. "You see, I don't need much. At a cent a word, two thousand words a week would bring in twenty dollars. I can manage on that."

"I don't want to dash your hopes," the poet said, "but I think I'd better caution you that editors aren't likely to accept everything you offer them. At least, not at first. However, I have a suggestion to offer you. Try writing for the magazines as well as the newspapers. *The Overland Monthly,* for instance, and some of the eastern magazines. Now is as good a time as any to start collecting rejection slips."

"Rejection slips?" Jack asked, puzzled.

George Sterling laughed. "These are little printed forms which, in artful language, regret that although your manuscript displays great talent, it does not quite fit the current needs of the magazine. I've a trunkful of them."

Jack and the poet left the library together and sat on a bench in the nearby park. Sterling spoke of books and of his associates, who were making names for themselves in the nation. The sun was low when they parted.

"Come and see me whenever you're in San Francisco, Jack," the poet said. "I'll see that you meet Ambrose Bierce, Joaquin Miller and the rest of the writing crowd. It'll do you good to talk shop once in a while."

As Jack turned homeward, his pace quickened. He was eager to get to his room and begin writing again. Once he had sold a few stories, he would have earned the right to talk shop with George Sterling and his friends.

He wondered how long it would take to sell a half-dozen manuscripts. A few weeks? Surely, it wouldn't take much more time than that. It was just a matter of working hard, and—he wasn't afraid of hard work.

Work Beast

⊆ EACH EVENING, RETURNING
from work at the jute mill, Jack asked eagerly
about his mail. The days slipped past and
none came, but he did not worry.

He could understand that newspapers might
not be able to publish an article immediately.
Give them time, he told himself; no news is
good news. At least he had not begun collecting those rejection slips George Sterling had
talked about. Besides, even if the editors were
to buy only half of the manuscripts which he
had sent, his earnings would enable him to
quit the jute mill.

At last, there came a long envelope from the *Call*. The moment he saw it, Jack knew that one of his articles was being returned. The envelope was too bulky to contain just a check. Perhaps the piece had been too long and the editor was sending it back to be shortened or changed in some manner.

Jack ripped open the envelope. The article about seal hunting in the Bering Sea had been returned without a word. There wasn't even a sign that it had been read; not even a rejection slip.

Yet Jack was not disheartened. After all there were those other manuscripts which he had sent out to the papers. Every one of them was fully as good as his prize-winning typhoon story. Surely, some of them would sell. After supper, fighting down the urge to sleep, he dipped his pen and began writing.

The next night he came home to find two more bulky envelopes containing rejected manuscripts. The following evening, there were two more. Before the week was over, all of his articles, like homing pigeons, were roosting on the table where they had been born.

"I'm got giving up," Jack told his mother, strangling his disappointment. "Both Miss Coolbrith and George Sterling tried to warn me, but I was listening with only one ear. I can see, now, I'm just a lubber at this business —green as grass. I've got to learn more about writing. I should find some kind of work that doesn't eat up all my time and doesn't take the edge off my wits."

Flora London interrupted: "Your father thinks he may receive that appointment as a special policeman. If he does, you'll be able to leave the jute mill."

Jack scarcely listened. He pointed to the *Help Wanted* section of the *Oakland Tribune* and began reading aloud: "Young man wanted, willing to start at bottom. Splendid opportunity for advancement." Putting the newspaper down, he went on: "It's with the Electric Railway. Now that kind of work would be interesting. I'd be learning something while I was earning my pay. I'd be getting into a trade which is becoming more important every day. It would be something I could always fall back on."

"You ought to look into it," his mother said quickly. "Why don't you take an hour off from the jute mill in the morning?"

"There probably will be a thousand men trying for a fine position like that . . ." He hesitated. "Just the same, I'm going, even if

it does mean getting in wrong with my foreman at the mill."

*   *   *

At seven o'clock the next morning, Jack
entered the head office at the power plant of
the Oakland Electric Railway. A clerk behind
the counter took his name and told him to
wait with several other young men who appeared to be seeking the same job. One by one,
they were called into an inner office from
which they quickly returned with disappointed
expressions.

When Jack's turn came, he was greeted
pleasantly by a portly man seated behind a big
desk. "Take a seat, young man." The man
gestured toward a chair. "Now, have you
had any experience with electricity?"

Jack's heart sank. If experience were
needed, he was through already. "No," he
said. "But there was no mention of experience."

"That's right." The man beamed. "You
see, we can overlook the matter of experience.
Mainly, what we want is a bright young man
with an eye on the future, a lad who's willing
to start at the bottom rung of the ladder.
Think you can fill the bill, young man?"

"Yes, sir. I'm not afraid of hard work."

The man gave a pleased nod. "That is the proper way to feel. So many lads want easy jobs—oiling or becoming an electrician's helper. I hope you aren't that impatient?"

"No—" Jack was wondering about the bottom rung.

"Good!" Leaning back in his chair, the man made a little speech. He said that coal was the life blood of the electric energy. It was coal which ran the steam engines which, in turn, turned great electric generators from which the street cars drew their power. "Coal is mighty important and the lad who handles it has a mighty important job. You can see that, eh?"

"Yes, sir."

"Fine. You'll be in charge of the coal, seeing to it that there is always plenty on hand for the fireman. Of course," he coughed, "the wage will be small, at first. Thirty dollars a month and a free pass to ride the cars. When can you begin?"

Jack did not reply at once. He wasn't sure that he wanted the job. The pay wasn't any more than he was receiving at the jute mill. Still, there was the promise: "Splendid opportunity for advancement." And since the hours probably would be shorter and he would be learning a skilled trade— "I can start tomorrow, sir."

"Tomorrow it is." The man rose. "Report for work in the fire room at seven."

*   *   *

Jack quickly discovered what being "in charge of the coal" meant. His tools were simple ones—a shovel and an iron wheelbarrow. His job was to fill the wheelbarrow at the coal bins and then trudge with it to the fire room where he dumped the load on the iron plates by the furnace.

He worked steadily, keeping the fireman—a grim, silent fellow—supplied with enough fuel for the furnace.

After about an hour, the foreman came by and said: "See here, you'll have to work faster than that." He pointed to the fire room wall. "Start an extra pile over there. Before you quit tonight, you got to have enough coal for the night fireman."

Jack wondered why the night fireman didn't have a coal passer of his own but, being new on the job, said nothing. The fireman kept up his unfriendly silence.

Jack quickened his pace, dumped one load on the plates for the furnaces and the next against the wall for the night fireman. He doubled his speed but, try as he might, he was unable to keep the grim fireman supplied if he worked at filling the night pile.

Dripping with sweat, grimy and choking from coal dust, Jack toiled on, hour after hour. There was no pause for lunch. The sandwiches he had brought had to be swallowed down while he was shoveling coal. As the afternoon wore on, every muscle protested, but he couldn't stop. He kept looking forward to the end of the ten-hour day.

At five, the night fireman arrived and the day man left. When Jack looked in vain for someone to take over his job, the foreman trotted up, looked at the pile of night coal and barked: "You ain't got enough coal there to last half the night. What ails you? Get busy, sonny. Stack it up halfway to the ceiling. Then you can quit."

Grimly, Jack turned to again. It was shovel, push, and dump—over and over. Darkness fell, the electric lights came on, and he continued working. His legs were trembling and his body was one mass of aching muscles. It wasn't until nine o'clock that he had stacked enough coal to keep the furnaces going until he returned in the morning.

"You can quit now," the foreman said.

Jack staggered out of the fire room, onto the street, and home. He fell asleep at the kitchen table before his mother finished cooking his supper. He was hardly aware of his father helping him to his room and putting him to bed. It seemed to him he'd hardly closed his eyes when he heard his mother calling out that it was six o'clock and time to go to work.

The next day was the same. And the next. Work, eat, sleep. He hardly listened when anyone spoke to him. That was his life. Pain racked his body. His wrists weakened and he had to strap them with leather bands to keep going. On his one Sunday off each month, he slept the clock around.

As he drove himself, he thought that, surely —any day now—he would be boosted up to the second rung of the railway company's ladder. Just a while longer, he kept telling himself, until the day came when he sank down on the fireroom floor and could not get up again. The fireman, who had said hardly a word to him during all the time he had been there, helped him to his feet.

"Son," the fireman said, "you'll not last long at this rate. I don't like to see a lad killing himself like you're doing, even if you did put two men out of work."

Jack blinked. "I—I put two men out of work? I don't know what you mean."

The fireman regarded him narrowly. "I guess you don't, at that." With a thin smile, he went on: "So, they took advantage of a green kid! Before you took this job, we had two coal passers here—both of 'em full-grown men with families. Each of 'em got forty dollars a month."

Jack wet his lips. "And that's why I was hired! To save the company fifty dollars a month."

"That's right, son. I suppose they promised you'd be president of the company some day?"

"Not in so many words." Jack grinned crookedly. "But I was fool enough to think something like that." He picked up his shovel. "I'll finish out the day. Then, I'm through."

"What will you do?" the fireman asked. "Jobs are mighty scarce with the panic on."

"I don't know. Maybe I'll be able to sign on a ship. I'd even go out on a sealer again. Anything would be better than being a work beast."

"I know what I'd do if I were out of work," the fireman said. "I'd join Kelly's Army." When Jack looked puzzled, he explained. "I guess you've been working so hard you haven't

read the papers.   This Charlie Kelly is round-
ing up an army of unemployed in San Francisco and Oakland.   He's named himself
general and is going to lead the way back East.
He says they'll all ride the rods and live off the
land like hoboes. Then, when they get to Ohio,
they'll join Coxey's Army for the march on
Washington."

"I might join Kelly, at that," Jack said
slowly.   "That is, if I can't find another job."
As he returned to his shoveling, he recalled
dimly that his father had gotten the appointment as a special policeman.   He had hardly
listened when his mother said that his earnings weren't so much needed now and begged
him to go back to studying and writing.

But he had been a work beast for so long
that the urge to write no longer stirred inside
of him.   Maybe Coxey and this new man, right
here in Oakland, could make things better for
working people with their marching armies.
Anyway, on the march he'd be free of drudgery
for a while.

He glanced toward the fireman.   "I think I
will join up with General Kelly."

School Days

⏣ THREE MONTHS LATER, JACK London returned home from the road, tanned and bright-eyed. His mother, holding out her arms to him, cried happily: "I've never seen you looking better, Jack!"

He grinned widely. "I've never felt better in all my life. I'm ready to buckle down and go to work."

"No more adventuring?" Flora London asked hopefully. "You've decided on what you're going to do for a living?"

He nodded. "I'm going to be an author."

His mother looked anxious. "You know that I want you to write, Jack, but writing for a living is so uncertain. It's not like having a steady job. Remember, you tried it, and—"

Jack laughed. "I didn't know the trade. I still don't, but—I'm going to learn. A sailor can't handle a schooner until he's learned navigation; a composer can't write the music you enjoy playing until he first learns the scales. It's the same with writing—an author can't get anywhere until he knows enough to use words well. Even a tramp has to know his business or he'll starve to death. I found that out on the road."

That evening, when John London came home, he wanted to hear all about his son's experiences.

"I was a real tramp, Pa," Jack said. "A hobo. General Kelly's Army got ahead of me and, in order to catch up, I had to hop a side-door Pullman—that's a boxcar—to Sacramento. There, I caught another freight to Reno. By then, the other hoboes were calling me the Sailor Kid."

Jack then told how he had worked his way eastward on freight and express trains, dodging brakemen, cooking "mulligan" in the hobo jungles, and sleeping in roundhouses, barns, or haystacks.

At Council Bluffs, in Iowa, he had finally caught up with Kelly's Army. With the others he had followed the Des Moines and Mississippi rivers as far as Louisville. There, the army began to break up. The hardships they had met caused the men to turn back by the hundreds. Only a handful of Kelly's men went on to Washington where they joined the few who had stayed with Coxey. Congress saw no reason to listen to the little road-weary band. Coxey was tossed into jail. People remained as hard up for work as before.

"After the march failed, I was on my own," Jack continued. "I caught a cattle train for Chicago, and a freight to New York." He went on to tell how he had zigzagged over the shining rails through Pennsylvania, Maryland, and Virginia. Then north, through Boston to Ottawa, and westward across Canada to Vancouver.

"I picked up a stoker's berth on a San Francisco-bound coasting steamer, and here I am. It was all pretty rough going," Jack said. "Sometimes, even worse than that. In Buffalo, I was thrown in jail simply because I had no job and no place to go. There were nights when I had no shelter from rain and snow;

there were times when I went hungry. But—" he smiled, "I'm glad I went. I found out what people are thinking and how good a lot of them are. You'd be surprised how many kindly people gave us handouts."

"You've seen a lot of America," John London said quietly.

Jack nodded. "I did more than look and listen. I've filled my notebooks. And I've done some thinking of my own. Hoboland," he said slowly, "is filled with all sorts of people— honest men and thieves, lazy men and bitter men. The difference between hoboes and other men is that the tramps—all of them— are running away from something.

"I wouldn't have missed this experience for anything, but I'll never go on the road again. I've got my course charted, now. Reading and studying, that's my line. And if I can find some sort of job to pay my way, I'll go through high school and enter the University of California."

"I think you can count on it, son," John London said, "now that my health has improved so much and I'm able to work steady."

*   *   *

Jack plunged into the adventure of learning

with all the energy at his command. He turned his bedroom into a study with reading lamp, bookshelves, writing pads, and sharpened pencils. Before many weeks had passed, he was able to enroll as a freshman at the Oakland High School where he worked as a part-time janitor. To add to his earnings he took every odd job he could find. Hard times were slowly coming to an end; men no longer stood in line at soup kitchens. Craftsmen were beginning to find work at their trades and no longer needed to compete for the kind of job that Jack could do between the hours of study.

He visited the Public Library to discuss his plans with Miss Coolbrith. But she was no longer there.

"She is living in San Francisco," said the new librarian, Frederick Irons Bamford. "Before she resigned, she spoke of you and your ambitions. She said that when you returned, she hoped I would help you in every way possible, and—" he smiled, "I promised her I'd do my best."

Mr. Bamford was as good as his word. He went from shelf to shelf with Jack, pointing out the works of the world's finest writers. He suggested that Jack read books dealing with history and government as well as stories drawn from the imagination.

"A writer must understand people," he explained. "He can do that only if he understands their needs and how they have worked through the ages for the satisfaction of those needs."

Mr. Bamford did more than help Jack choose books. He introduced him to one of the younger librarians—Fred Jacobs, and in time the two became good friends.

Jack had need for friendship because at high school the boys and girls gave him a wide berth. They had no place for this shabbily dressed sun-bronzed stranger who scrubbed floors and washed windows while they played games in the schoolyard.

Even when he had articles published in the high school paper, his fellow students made no gestures of friendship. They read the accounts of his experiences at sea and on the road in the *Aegis,* but they didn't ask how he'd had time to write them, and go to school, and do janitor's work, and other part-time jobs.

Not even Fred Jacobs knew that Jack rose an hour earlier than he had to every morning to write. It didn't matter that he would receive no pay for these writings. He was learning his trade. That was the important thing, he told himself.

Of course, he had Jenny Prentiss to talk to, and Eliza and her husband, and Pete, the fisherman. And once in a while, his boyhood playmate, Frank Atherton, came up from Los Gatos for a short visit. But mostly, Jack traveled the lonesome road.

Then, suddenly, Jack's friendship with Fred Jacobs brought him into a group of young people whose interests were very much like his own. It all began one Sunday afternoon when the two happened to walk out of the library together.

"I don't know how you manage it!" Fred remarked. "You're not only rushing through high school like a house afire, but you're working at a half-dozen jobs. And judging by the number of books you take out, you still have plenty of time to read. I'm beginning to wonder if you ever sleep."

"I wish I didn't have to spend so much time sleeping," Jack answered with a laugh.

Fred, however, was not joking. He had thought a good deal about Jack's problems. "The routine of the school isn't geared to your pace. I think—when you're a bit further along, you should cram for the university exams and skip the remainder of high school."

"Say—" Jack stopped in his tracks. "That's an idea! Just how hard are the entrance examinations at California?"

"They aren't easy, Jack. The University demands that you pass a wide range of subjects for entrance. I've known students who've failed to pass even after a year at one of the big cramming schools."

"When," Jack asked, "will the next examinations be held?"

"In August."

"That will give me three months. I think I can do it, now that school vacation is about to start. I'd be sure of it if I weren't such a lubber when it comes to mathematics."

Fred shook his head. "It can't be done, Jack."

"Why can't it be done? I'm used to hard work."

"Well—if you're really serious about it, I'll help you with science. And I know someone who can coach you in math. However, if I were you, I'd go to one of the private cramming schools, too. Of course, that would take money."

"I might be able to arrange it. Now, what about this mathematics teacher, Fred? How much does he charge? If it isn't too much, I'd like to see him right away so that I can get started."

"Hurry, hurry, hurry," Fred said with a chuckle. "All right, we'll go to see about it. I'm quite sure there won't be any charge whatsoever. Bess is a lovely girl . . ."

"A girl?" Jack frowned and hung back. "I'm not exactly used to girls, Fred."

"Come on." Fred took Jack's arm. "She won't bite you."

Still hesitating, Jack walked along at Fred's side. After a short walk, Fred halted at a neat white house surrounded by a well-kept garden. Fred led the way through the garden path to the front door and lifted the knocker. A moment later when the door swung open, Jack saw a slender dark-eyed girl.

Jack managed an awkward bow when Fred introduced him to Bess Maddern. He was too embarrassed to listen to Fred's easy chatter as the girl led the way into a large and handsome room. The fine furniture and big piano made him more uncomfortable than ever. Then suddenly his eyes fell on shelves filled with books. With books, he was always at home.

He moved forward to take a look at the titles and then became aware of Fred's voice. "And

Jack seems to think that passing the entrance exams at U. C. is as simple as oyster pirating or catching seals."

"Won't you sit down, Mr. London?" Bess Maddern said.

Jack lowered himself stiffly, sitting on the edge of the chair, near the huge fireplace.

The girl said: "I'm so glad Fred brought you. Edward Applegarth and his sister, Mabel, are dropping in later. I know they'll be anxious to meet the author of those fine adventure stories which have been appearing in *The Aegis*. Are you writing for any other magazines?"

"I've tried, Miss Maddern—" Jack settled down in his chair. "I guess I just haven't got the hang of the writing trade, yet."

"But he's building up a good, solid foundation, Bess," Fred put in. "He reads more books in a night than we do in a week. He soaks up ideas like a sponge. He's a drayhorse when it comes to work and study, but I don't see how he can be ready for the August examinations."

"He can try," the girl said, looking at Jack with a smile. "Don't let Fred discourage you. I'll be glad to help you with mathematics, and

Mabel Applegarth can give you help with English. She's taking special courses at the University."

As she went on, Jack forgot he was talking to a girl who lived in the finest house he'd ever entered. Before long, they were discussing the books they had read. They talked about Mark Twain and the other writers whose talents had first come to fruition in San Francisco.

Then Jack asked: "Have you read anything by this English author, Rudyard Kipling? There's a man who can sling words." He broke off. He'd have to watch himself. Slang was all right in a ship's forecastle or in a hobo jungle, but not in surroundings like these.

Yet, when Bess began drawing him out about his travels, he was at it again. He heard himself using the language of the sea and the road. The funny part was that this girl did not seem to mind.

Finally, Fred Jacobs interrupted. "The way you two have been going, I haven't been able to get a word in edgewise. But now—" he nodded toward the window, "here come the Applegarths. Jack, you're not going to be able to out-talk Ted, or Mabel, either."

Bess Maddern went out to open the door

to her friends and Jack heard laughing voices in the hall.

"This is Ted Applegarth," Fred said, as a handsome young man strode into the room.

The newcomer gripped Jack's hand and then, glancing at Fred said, "Mabel will be in as soon as she fixes her hair. Seems like one wispy curl got blown an eighth of an inch southwest by the wind." Turning back to Jack, he went on, "Speaking of wind, I read that typhoon piece of yours. It was real red meat. I hear you've been in Yokohama. I'd like to hear more about it."

Jack began telling his impressions of the Japanese city. Ted's unmistakable interest gave him confidence and he was getting along famously until Bess Maddern and her friend entered the room. Then he broke off awkwardly in the middle of a sentence.

As Bess Maddern introduced him to Mabel Applegarth, Jack felt that he was all hands and feet. He stumbled as he went back to his chair and sat tongue-tied, while the talk drifted in a mist around him.

He listened to Mabel Applegarth's beautiful voice with its hint of an English accent and thought her comments about McKinley and

Bryan very witty. You wouldn't think a girl with gold hair like a sunrise would know enough to talk so wisely about the men who were running for President.

When she paused, her brother and Fred carried on in the same bright mood. Then the talk turned to the future of those "horseless carriages" which, now and then, could be seen snorting and banging in the streets.

Jack sat there silently, very conscious of his rough clothes, his work-scarred hands, and his general awkwardness. Although he was interested, he said nothing when the others mentioned the rumors of a great gold discovery in Alaska.

Suddenly Mabel Applegarth addressed him directly. "What do you think, Mr. London? Do you believe there's any truth to the story?"

He swallowed hard. "Of course, I ain't sure, but—" He bit his lips. Why had he said "ain't?" He knew better. He thought he saw an amused smile on Mabel's face.

Bess Maddern changed the subject and the talk flowed on. Jack shut up like a clam. He wasn't going to make a fool of himself again. Not in front of a beautiful girl like Mabel Applegarth.

Just before the Applegarths left, Bess explained about Jack's intention to take the university examinations. "Perhaps, Mabel, you could coach him in English?"

"Why, I'd be glad to," Mabel replied. She smiled at Jack. "We could start next Tuesday. You'll come to dinner, won't you?"

"I . . ."

"We'll be expecting you," Ted Applegarth said heartily. "I intend to hear more about those adventures you've had. So it's all settled."

"He'll be there," Fred Jacobs said, walking out to the hall with them.

Bess Maddern smiled at Jack encouragingly. "You couldn't find a better English coach than Mabel. Now, before you leave, I'll get you some books that will help you with mathematics. If you could come by a couple of nights each week, I think you could get through the course."

As he walked up the street with Fred Jacobs, Jack mopped his brow. "That was quite an afternoon," he said. "I'm glad you took me there, Fred, even if I don't belong in the same class as those girls."

"What are you talking about?" Fred snapped. "They're just girls."

Just girls? They were much more than that,

Jack thought. They were wonderful human beings. He'd have to work harder than ever to earn the respect of people like that. And he'd work, all right. He would pass the entrance examinations. His arm tightened about the books which Bess Maddern had lent him. Already he was planning the hours of study. Five hours sleep was all he needed. That would give him nineteen hours a day.

"We've got the rest of the evening ahead of us, Jack," Fred Jacobs was saying. "How about taking in a show? This may be your last chance for quite a while. Tomorrow you're going to have to start studying."

"I'm starting tonight," Jack said.

First Term

⚓ IT WAS AN AFTERNOON IN
mid-August and a cooling northwest wind
blew across San Francisco Bay and the Oakland Estuary. Pete, the fisherman, whistled
cheerfully as he went about his task of painting an upturned dory. Hearing footsteps on
the dock, he looked up.

"Jack!" he exclaimed. "You look so different." He eyed Jack with concern. "What
makes you so skinny, your face so white? You
been working again at the cannery or the jute
place?"

"Nothing like that. I've been studying."

"Study, hey? I know you always read books, but why do you study so hard and make yourself sick?"

"I'm not really sick. Just a little tired. You see, I had only three months to get ready for the examinations at the University."

"So that's it. You want to go to college and learn to write books yourself. You pass those examinations?"

Jack nodded. "I passed." He sighed wearily. "And now I feel as though I never want to look at a book again. I'm going to have to rest up before I start in at college." He glanced longingly out at the bay. "If I had a boat of my own, I'd go sailing for a few days."

"That's a fine idea, Jack. For you, there is no finer medicine than salt water. And you don't need a boat of your own. Look!" He pointed to a small craft nudging the pilings at the next wharf. "That one belongs to my boy, Tony. Now he has a job in San Francisco and never sails her any more. You take that skiff."

Jack brightened. "Thanks, Pete. I'll run along home and get fishing tackle and some food."

"You don't need to go home. Come here."
He pulled Jack into the wharf shed. "I fix
you up good. Here, nice Italian bread, coffee,
ham—" He put the food in a wooden box and
then wrapped up some sardines in a newspaper. "Good bait for fishing. In the stern
locker of that skiff, you'll find fishing lines,
blankets for sleeping . . ."

"Pete, how can I thank you?"

"Don't you thank me. Go along, now.
Don't you worry about anything. After a
while, I will stop by your house and tell your
mother where you are gone. And don't you
come back until your eyes sparkle good again.
You hear?"

Jack dropped into the skiff and cast off, and
headed the little skiff toward Goat Island.
There he anchored in one of the small coves
and began fishing for rock cod. With several
big ones in the bottom of the boat, he cast off
again and sailed north for a beach he knew of
on Angel Island.

It was dusk by the time he hauled the skiff
ashore and started a driftwood fire. With the
coffeepot on, and one of the rock cod roasting
on the coals, Jack gazed out at the bay, rosy-
stained in the glowing sunset. The weariness

from the long weeks of study fell away. "Like that schooner," Jack thought, "melting in the shadows of the Sausalito hills."

After he had eaten, he rolled into his blankets and slept under a million stars. The sun was high when he awakened and he jumped with the awful thought that he was wasting time. Then he remembered where he was, and that he had earned the right to a rest. Now that the long hours of anxious study were over, he could take pride in his accomplishment. Even Bess Maddern hadn't believed that he could complete the work of a two-year high school course in three months.

After a swim in the bay and breakfast, Jack sailed north into San Pablo Bay. At Benicia, he found old friends in the Fish Patrol. Charlie Le Grant immediately offered him a patrolman's job.

"Thanks, Charlie," Jack said. "If I were taking a longer vacation, I'd accept. But pretty soon, it's back to the battle of the books."

He sailed on up into the waters of the San Joaquin and Sacramento rivers, exploring the islands in Suisun Bay. He pitched camp when he felt like it and talked with the fishermen, flatboatmen and farmers he met along the way. Then, south again, running down past

San Francisco along the San Mateo Coast to the lower bay.

For two weeks he wandered—sailing and fishing and yarning. He swam in the crisp cold water and slept in the open air. When he returned the skiff to its berth, Pete grinned with satisfaction, saying: "I guess you feel pretty good, hey?"

Jack nodded, full of quiet confidence. "I could lick my weight in wildcats. I'll take every course they can offer at the University and yell for more. At night, I'll start pouring out the stories. Watch my smoke, Pete."

*   *   *

Jack knew that he could count on only one term at the University, and tried to cram every single course he could into those precious months. "English, history, philosophy, the natural science," he told Bess Maddern one evening. "Those are the things that put meat on a writer's literary bones. When I think about that first article I wrote—the one about the typhoon—"

"The writing showed talent and imagination, Jack," Bess said. "With only paper and ink, you made the typhoon seem real."

He shrugged. "It was a lubberly piece of work. If I had known about the forces that make those storms—" He shrugged. "Knowledge is what is needed for success in writing, or anything else. Knowledge, and the wit to make use of it. That's where philosophy and history come in."

"Jack," she murmured, "aren't you taking on too much at once?"

"I have to," Jack replied. "My father is failing and won't be able to work much longer. I may not be able to stay at U. C. after this term. Of course, if I can make some money writing, I can continue on at college and help my family out at the same time. That's what I'm working and hoping for. I don't want to go back to being an unskilled laborer."

"You'll win through, Jack," Bess said softly, confidently.

Bess Maddern's faith increased his confidence in himself. He always left her feeling more secure. It was different with Mabel Applegarth. In her presence, he was uncomfortably aware of his shortcomings.

However, when he commented on this to Fred Jacobs, Fred smiled. "You have to admit that Mabel has knocked some of the rough edges off you, Jack."

"Maybe that's it," Jack admitted honestly. "Maybe I don't like feeling grateful."

For all his misgivings, the hours spent with the Applegarths and Bess were the happiest he had ever known. With them he entered at once into the challenging, spirited debates at the Henry Clay Debating Society. In defending his ideas before the members of the society he became clearer in his own thinking.

In addition to his college work, Jack burned the midnight oil writing stories and articles. He mailed the manuscripts to newspapers and magazines. Yet, when the term drew to a close, he had to face up to the fact that he had not sold anything.

One day Jack was grimly counting up his rejection slips. Mabel Applegarth said, "I think the reason why editors don't buy your work is because you choose such disagreeable subjects to write about."

"But," Jack protested, "I can only write about life the way I see it. I can't do those love stories you see in the magazines. I didn't grow up listening to drawing room talk."

"Still," she said, "you could have happy endings. Why did you have that hunter die in your sealing story?"

"Because it was the whole point of the story," Jack explained. "He had to die as he did."

Mabel shook her head. "Jack, if you expect to sell your stories, you'll have to write the kind that editors want. You'll have to learn to write about pleasant things and pleasant people."

"Fluff!" Jack exclaimed. "You've read Kipling, haven't you? And he doesn't write creampuff stories, neither does Mark Twain nor Ambrose Bierce."

Jack saw a smile cross Mabel's face. He flushed and went on lamely, "I don't mean to put myself in Kipling's class. But I do think that if I keep on going I'll be able to sell enough of my stuff to make ends meet for myself and my family. I believe that if I give it full time . . ."

"Does that mean you're planning to leave college?" Mabel asked.

"Yes. I'll have to get the rest of my education out of the free library. The way things are, I can't afford to continue at U. C."

*   *   *

When the term ended, Jack went to work on an old battered typewriter which Captain Shepard lent him. He wrote stories, articles, and even poetry. He mailed the manuscripts out to the *Overland Monthly*, *The Black Cat*, *Youth's Companion*, and other magazines.

He wrote about the oyster pirates and the Fish Patrol, about the *Sophie Sutherland* and his adventures in hoboland. He rarely left his writing table except for his meals, or a visit to the library.

He said to his mother one evening: "Some of the magazines pay up to ten cents a word. But I'll be satisfied with a penny a word even if I sell only a quarter of what I write."

"But suppose—" his mother began.

"Suppose they don't buy anything?" Jack laughed. "They will. Sooner or later, they will!"

"That's the spirit, son," John London said. "Don't you worry about Jack, Flora. he'll win out."

The weeks passed and Jack continued to write feverishly. And then the thick envelopes began coming back. At first one or two came each day. Then, the flood. Dismayed, Jack stared at the stack of rejection slips on his writing table.

Time had run out on him. He didn't even have enough money left for stamps and envelopes. He would have to give up—for a while. He'd get a job and save every cent and then— he'd try again.

That afternoon, Jack appeared at his sister's

house to return Captain Shepard's typewriter. "I'll not be needing this for a while," he told Captain Shepard.

"You certainly won't, Jack," Eliza's husband roared. "Not if you're willing to go partners with me. Look here."

Captain Shepard's desk was cluttered with newspaper clippings and maps.

"I'm going to the Klondike." Captain Shepard's eyes were alight. "By George, I'm going to get my share of that gold. But I'm not as spry as I used to be and I need a partner like you. Will you go with me, Jack?"

"I haven't heard much about the gold rush," Jack said. "I've been too busy to read the newspapers."

"It's a big thing," Captain Shepard interrupted. "Listen to this—"

His brother-in-law told how fortunes were being made along the Yukon and Klondike rivers. The whole country was headed north to the gold fields.

"It's bigger than the California rush of '49, Jack. The creeks are said to be loaded with gold nuggets. I've already gotten a loan on this house and so we don't have to worry about money. We've got a grubstake."

He unfolded a map. "We can go in by the

Juneau route, to Dyea and over the Chilkoot Pass. Then, when we reach Dawson City, we'll strike out and stake our claims. We can beat the freeze if we take passage on the *Umatilla.* She's leaving San Francisco for Seattle in four days. What do you say, Jack?"

Jack did not hesitate. "I'm with you, Captain. All the way." He was breathing faster. Here was not only a chance to get the money he needed to go on with his writing, but here was adventure, too!

They were listing the items needed for their outfit when Eliza returned from the grocery store. She said to Jack: "He shouldn't go. The doctor says that his heart is bad."

"I'm spry enough, I won't strain my heart," her husband said with a smile. "Haven't I said I wouldn't pick up any big nuggets? Didn't I promise you to take only the small ones?"

Eliza sighed and turned toward Jack. "He's determined to go. I can't stop him. And so, I'm counting on you, Jack. You'll look out for him, won't you?"

The Klondike

⏹ ON A BLEAK GRAY MORNING in August, Jack London found himself on the beach at Dyea. The Chilkoot Indian village was north of Juneau, on the narrow southeastern Panhandle of Alaska. All around him men swarmed, shouting and laughing excitedly as they pitched their tents. Great stacks of supplies littered the shoreline. Wolfish-looking dogs snarled and barked. Fur-clad Indians bargained with the goldseekers.

Jack's eyes were shining. Adventure lay ahead. As he drove a tent stake with a hammer, he said, "This is it—the jumping-off place for Dawson City and the gold fields."

"Some jump," his companion, Jim Goodman, said. "Six hundred miles through some mighty rough country."

Jim Goodman was one of a party of three prospectors who had formed a partnership with Jack and Captain Shepard during the passage from San Francisco. The other two prospectors, Merritt Sloper and Fred Thompson, had gone into the village with Captain Shepard to arrange for porters to help them pack in over the lofty Chilkoot Pass.

Jack glanced northward toward the snow-capped peaks of the Alaskan coastal range. "It won't be so bad, Jim, once we get our supplies over to Lake Linderman," he said. "From what I hear, there's plenty of timber and we can build a boat. From Linderman on, it's downstream through the lakes, the Lewes River and the Yukon to Dawson."

Goodman nodded as he pulled a tent rope taut. "Merritt Sloper's a first-rate ship's carpenter. You're a sailor, and the rest of us are handy with tools. We'll make it all right. The only thing is—I'm worried about that partner of yours. Anyone can see with half an eye that Cap isn't a well man."

"His heart's bad," Jack said. "He's pretty

sick and he's trying to keep the rest of us from knowing it. However, so far as the work goes, you don't have to worry. I'll do his share."

"It isn't that, Jack. The captain's a real decent sort and I'd hate to see anything happen to him. Doctors are scarcer'n hen's eggs where we are going, and—" Jim looked up. "They're coming back. Let's hope they got hold of some porters so that we can get under way."

When Captain Shepard reached the tent with his two companions, he said glumly: "Things look bad. In San Francisco, we were told that the Indians would pack us in over the Pass for six cents a pound. Now they're asking forty cents a pound."

"Forty cents!" Jim Goodman exclaimed. "Why that's robbery!"

"There's no bargaining with 'em," Merritt Sloper growled. "They've got all the work they can handle and so—it's take it or leave it."

Jack looked over the pile of supplies. There were sacks of flour, cornmeal, and beans; coffee, sugar, dried fruits, and salt. Soap, matches, blankets, clothing, and cooking vessels. Guns, gold-pans, axes, carpenter's tools, nails—every article was needed if they were to reach the gold fields and stay alive through six months of bitter Klondike weather.

"I estimate we have about eight thousand pounds," he said.

"And," Fred Thompson muttered, "as I figure it, that will cost us over three thousand dollars if the Indians do the packing over the trail. I, for one, haven't got that kind of money."

"Me, neither," Merritt Sloper said. "Anyway, I came up here to find gold, not to dish it out."

Jack spoke up. "The only thing to do is pack in ourselves." He grinned. "I guess I'm as strong as any Chilkoot Indian. We'll hire a boat and tow our stuff upstream to the foot of the Pass. After that, we'll just have to carry it on our backs the way the Indians do."

Merritt Sloper said, "Having to do it all by ourselves will take weeks."

"A month, probably," Jack said. "Well, we'd better get started. Otherwise, the freeze is going to catch us somewhere between here and Dawson City and we'll be snowed in for the winter."

Later that day, they rented an old flatboat and hove to with the job of loading and then towing the supplies upstream. All that day, and the next, they toiled.

Captain Shepard tried but he could not keep up with the others. He saw Jack was doing two men's work to spare him.

That night he said, "I want to go on, but— I haven't the right. I would be holding the rest of you back." He bit his lips. "Good luck, boys. If I leave now, I'll be able to catch the steamer for San Francisco."

It took Jack and his three partners over five weeks to cover the twenty-odd miles to Lake Linderman. Rain fell almost constantly as they struggled up the steep, rocky trail, carrying bulky packs weighing a hundred and fifty pounds each. Lurching and slipping, they fought their way upward and at the end of each mile, they dropped their supplies and went back for another load.

As he fought his way up through the Pass, Jack saw dozens of gold-seekers turn back. Stripped to the waist, he plunged on, outpacing many a Chilkoot porter.

Over the top of the Pass they went, then down across glaciers, over rocky cliffs, through hip-deep icy streams. Finally, the day came when glaciers and rocks were left behind and the party made camp near Lake Linderman.

Merritt Sloper looked up at the forest of tall straight spruce trees. "Prime timber, boys," he said, rubbing his hands. "Give me a few weeks and I'll build you as neat a craft as you ever laid eyes on."

Two fairly small flatboats were decided on. Under the carpenter's watchful eye, the trees were felled, trimmed, and cut into planks. The sound of axes, the snorting of whipsaws, and the banging of hammers filled the forest from dawn until dark.

When the last nail had been driven home and the canvas sails set, the boats were named the *Yukon Belle* and *Belle of the Yukon*. That was when Merritt Sloper stood back and gazed at his work. "I could've done a better job, given more time," he muttered. "Still, they'll do."

Jack heard a note of pride in Sloper's voice. Well, the little ship's carpenter, he thought, had a right to be proud. With few tools, deep in the Alaskan wilderness, Merritt Sloper had taken nature's trees and created something desperately needed.

"No man could've done better, Merritt," Jack said warmly and the others agreed.

Flushing, the carpenter said, "Thanks, boys. I guess it's up to Jack from now on. I build 'em, Jack sails 'em. What say we shove off in the morning? I think I smell gold."

At dawn, deep-laden with supplies, the boats set out. At the northern tip of Lake Linderman, all hands waded ashore. They had to drag boats and supplies a mile overland to Lake Bennett. Waterborne again, they sailed north to the Canadian border where, at Lake Marsh, a mounted policeman stopped them to look over their supplies.

Food was scarce in the Klondike, the mountie explained. He had orders to turn back anyone who didn't have at least seven hundred pounds of supplies.

"We don't want anyone to starve," he said. "Now you fellows are all right. However, if you take my advice, you'll get along before the freeze catches you. And watch out for White Horse Rapids. That's a dangerous stretch of water."

They sailed on, down the Lewes River to the point where it narrowed and flowed swiftly through the entrance to Miles Canyon. As they drew closer to the White Horse Rapids, they saw other boats drawn up on the rocky banks of the river. Hoarse shouts warned of the dangers which lay ahead.

"We'll pull in somewhere around here," Jack said. "I'd like to have a good look at the rapids before we tackle them."

Ashore, they were surrounded by dozens of gold-seekers. One black-bearded man muttered, "I'm telling you, boys, it's murder. Three boats lost yesterday and all hands drowned. We're waiting for some expert boatmen who know these rapids. You fellows had better do the same thing."

But Jack was full of confidence. With Jim Goodman and Sloper, he walked along the canyon's rim, looking down at the wild waters frothing through the narrows below. Here and there, caught in the rocks, was the smashed wreckage of other boats.

"Man alive," breathed Jim Goodman. "Just hit one of them rocks and you're a goner!"

"We'll stay clear of the rocks," Jack said. "Let's go back and get started."

"You mean to say you're going through? Don't you think we better wait until those experts get here?" Sloper asked.

"We'll make it," Jack said. "The current will keep us clear. It's only when you start to fight it that you get in trouble."

Hundreds of awed onlookers lined the cliffs as the *Yukon Belle* put out from shore and headed downstream. Jack was in the stern handling the steering oar, Merritt Sloper in the bow with a paddle. Fred Thompson and Jim Goodman sat amidships at the oars.

"Lean on the oars," Jack shouted. "Speed's what we need."

The roar of the river grew as the *Yukon Belle* drove toward the main channel. Jack stood, legs apart, his eyes gleaming, as the canyon walls flashed past. Faster and faster the flatboat went, leaping and plunging madly as the current gripped her.

An oar broke and the boat twisted toward the rocks. Jack, leaning on the steering oar, steadied her. She raced on, missing rocks by inches.

It could have been hours, minutes, or mere seconds since they started. Time meant nothing to Jack. His senses were keyed only on one thing: to defeat a force bent upon destroying him. It wasn't until he heard the hoarse cheers of the onlookers that he knew he'd shot the rapids.

As the *Yukon Belle* ran into the calm waters below and nudged the bank, he grinned. "Next time," he said, "will be easier. Let's go back for the other boat. Then we'll be through."

With both flatboats safely downriver, Jack soon found himself surrounded by goldseekers begging for his help in running the rapids. He and his companions spent several days bringing boats through the dangerous channel. However, they couldn't stay on to help them all. Winter was fast approaching and Dawson City was still nearly four hundred miles away.

As the wind and current took the travelers northward, Jack realized that the days were becoming shorter and the temperature was dropping. Old Man Winter was breathing down their necks when they crossed Lake Le Barge. A blizzard was blowing up as they entered the headwaters of the Yukon River.

The freeze caught them near Henderson Creek, about eighty miles from Dawson City. There they waited out the storm in an abandoned log cabin. Almost overnight the river froze and snow blanketed the Yukon Territory.

"I guess this is the end of the trail," said Jim Goodman, "until the thaw comes next spring. Let's dig in, boys."

During the weeks that followed, other parties of goldseekers drifted in and occupied other long-deserted cabins. Finally, the campsite took on the look of a village. The ring of axes resounded in the forest as the men chopped wood for their fireplaces. The smell of woodsmoke was mixed with the scent of bacon and beans, or moosemeat when a hunter was lucky.

Jack had not expected he would have much time for reading and writing, yet he had brought a few books along, as well as paper and pencils. When he unpacked them, Thompson laughed. "I never figured you for a reading man, Jack. A big, husky fellow like you! I always thought people who could sling words around were sissies."

Jack laughed and wished Mabel Applegarth were around to hear his companions' slang. It was a far cry from her drawing room and well-kept garden, to this log cabin in a snowbound wilderness. Here, in the frozen Klondike, it was hard to recall a world of witty debates with his university friends, of hours of struggle to get his exact meaning into a sentence, of mailing manuscripts and collecting rejection slips.

Nevertheless, all that winter, before the blazing fire, Jack took notes of everything he saw, heard, and did. He put down his impressions of the blizzards which came screaming across the Yukon and of the great white silences.

Their cabin became a sort of meeting place —not only for the men of the camp, but for any stranger who appeared out of the bleakness. French Canadian fur trappers, wandering Indians, hard-bitten Alaskan prospectors driving their teams of snarling huskies, Canadian Mounted Policemen—all were welcome to a warm meal and dry blankets.

Sometimes Jack joined in the fireside talk but mostly, he listened to these men of the North. Their words, their gestures became a part of him. With a half-smile he told himself that even if he failed to find gold nuggets, he still would have found riches here in the Klondike country.

*   *   *

Jack couldn't believe it when he took sick. Illness was a new experience to him. He couldn't understand why he had trouble dragging himself out of his bunk each morning, why his muscles ached.

"I think you're sick." Fred Thompson gave Jack an anxious look.

"No, Fred. It's just that I've gone soft.

I'll be all right as soon as the thaw comes and I can get out and do a man's work."

"That day isn't far off!" Fred exclaimed. "According to the old hands, we'll be able to do some prospecting along the creeks in another week or so."

"The sooner the better," Jack said, trying to match Fred's eagerness.

As the days passed, Jack had to drive himself to do his share when they worked along the banks of Henderson Creek. There, with pick and shovel, they had to break through the frozen ground to reach the gravel below.

He looked up dully the day Fred Thompson shouted, "Come here! Look at these gold specks in my pan. We've struck pay dirt!"

Before Jack reached his patrner's side, a gaunt old prospector put down his pick and peered into Fred Thompson's pan. "Iron pyrites," he grunted.

"Fool's gold," Jack said glumly. "That's all we'll ever find. We may as well quit."

"Quit!" Jim Goodman stiffened. "I never thought I'd ever see the day when you would use that word. Jack London, who packed in over Chilkoot Pass, who shot White Horse Rapids, and—"

"Take it easy, Jim," Fred Thompson said. "Jack's sick. Plenty sick. I kind of figured he was, but I wasn't sure of it until I thought I'd struck gold and let out that yell. I saw his face, Jim. Pyrites or gold—Jack just didn't care."

"What are we standing around talking for?" Merritt Sloper asked. "Let's push back to camp and get him to Doc Harvey."

*   *   *

"It's scurvy," Doctor Harvey said to Fred Thompson. "My partner went down with it, too. That's why I packed him off to Dawson City where he could get fresh vegetables. That's the cure. But young London's case is much more serious than Bert's." He turned to Jack. "You let it go on too long. Why did you keep it to yourself?"

"I thought it would pass," Jack said tonelessly.

"It won't. It will only get worse. Men die of scurvy. You'll have to go to Dawson. Of course, fruits and vegetables are worth their weight in gold in this part of the world, but— I think we might manage to cure you." Dr. Harvey explained that he was soon leaving for Dawson City himself and he planned to

make some money by taking a log raft down the Yukon.

"Logs bring a good price in Dawson. If you'll give me a hand taking down this log cabin of mine, making a raft of it and poling it to Dawson City, I'll give you a share of the profits."

Jack didn't want to leave his partners, but there was nothing else he could do. He couldn't go on as he had been, sick in mind and body.

With the help of several of the other gold-seekers, Dr. Harvey's cabin was quickly dismantled and made into a raft. Before the week was out, Jack and the doctor were drifting down the Yukon.

The doctor saw how dull and dispirited Jack was and said gently. "You'll be all right, Jack, after you've been in Dawson City a while. But, until then, you can't expect to care much about anything."

Yet Jack did have a flicker of interest one night when they stopped for camp. Louis Bond, a fellow Californian from Santa Clara, welcomed them cordially. "Just in time for supper," he said. "However, I have to feed the dogs first."

Jack's eyes went to the man's team and his gaze was held by the lead dog. The animal didn't look at all like the wolfish Alaskan huskies who were his companions; he towered above them, muscles rippling under sleek brown and white fur.

"Quite a dog!" Jack said.

"Buck is half St. Bernard and half Scotch shepherd," Bond said. "You should see him make those huskies behave on the trail. I wouldn't sell him for all the gold in the Klondike."

"Neither would I if he were mine." Jack looked down into Buck's eyes and bending over, began stroking the soft fur. The dog responded happily, wagging its tail furiously.

Jack couldn't forget Buck. Often, during his stay in Dawson, he thought about the dog that had been brought by its master all the way from sunny California to lead a dog team over the icy Klondike trails. Some day, he thought, he would write a story about a dog like Buck.

Fresh vegetables and meat and fruit were scarce in Dawson City and it was soon clear to Dr. Harvey that Jack would never be able to regain his health in the Klondike.

"I don't like to say this, Jack, but you've got to get out. I know how you hate to give up anything once you've started it, but scurvy's got the upper hand on you and this is no place to cure it."

Jack nodded slowly. He'd go out. He'd go out without as single nugget of gold in his pockets. Still, perhaps, the Klondike had given him something more valuable than yellow metal. His brain was stirring again with the urge to create, to express himself.

"I'll go, Doctor," he said. "I'll go just as soon as I can find a boat or a dog team headed for the outside."

Call of the Wild

Jack London came out of the Klondike in an open boat, sailing nearly two thousand miles down the Yukon River to St. Michaels, on the Bering Sea. A stoker's job on a coastal vessel took him south to Puget Sound. From Seattle, he beat his way to Oakland by riding the rods on the freight trains.

He arrived home to learn that his father had been dead for several weeks.

"He always believed in you," Flora London said, and she repeated what her husband had said just before he died.

"Jack will come out all right, Flora," John London had said. "And come out big, mark my words. He'll make a success of the Klondike, whether he digs it out of the grass roots or not."

Jack swallowed a lump in his throat. His father had guessed that he'd go back to his writing richer in experience than he had been before.

All during his voyage down the Yukon, stories had been taking shape in his mind— stories that were waiting to be written. Yet the odds against him were greater than ever. He was still weak from his illness and, with his father gone, it was up to him to take care of his mother. He would have to find work— any sort of work—and quickly, before he could even think about writing again.

But steady work, Jack soon discovered, was as hard to find as gold in the Klondike. Times were bad again. There were no openings, not even in the canneries or jute mills. Odd jobs were all that Jack could get—beating carpets, cleaning stables, washing windows. He did not go near the University or look up any of his young literary friends. His whole mind was taken up with making a living for his mother.

Eliza helped, and so did Jenny Prentiss, but Jack knew that times were hard for them, too.

"This can't go on," he said one evening. Fresh fruits and vegetables had restored his health and fighting spirit. "Tomorrow, I'm going back to my old plan—five hours sleep and the rest of the day at my typewriter. With nineteen hours a day, I'll have time to study and write as well as earn money."

"But Jack," his mother said, "you tried that before. Why don't you plan to get steady work? You could take one of the civil service examinations for mail carrier or something like that."

Jack shook his head. "This time I'm fighting the battle to the finish. I'll win through. I know I will."

"But, if you don't . . ."

"That will be time enough to go after a mailman's job." Jack grinned. "In the meantime, I'll keep the post office busy carrying my stories to the editors."

Once again, manuscripts littered his worktable as stories, articles, and poetry poured from his brain. Between part time jobs during the day, he was at the library, studying the new books and magazines, and listening to Mr. Bamford's advice.

"It might be well, Jack," the librarian told him, "to copy the work of the finest authors. Robert Louis Stevenson did that and his own way of expressing himself finally emerged."

Faithfully, Jack copied page after page from Kipling, Stevenson, and the other famous writers of the day. Whenever he came upon a word he did not understand, he pulled out his dictionary and wrote down the word and its meaning on a slip of paper. Soon, dozens of strips of paper containing lists of words were tacked to his walls, hung over his bed from strings, or pasted to his mirror. When he glanced up from his typewriter, his eyes would travel to these words.

Jack set himself a goal of writing at least a thousand words a day, although he often wrote five times that amount. Far into the night, his borrowed typewriter clattered, turning out stories of the Klondike, the sea, and the road. When a story or an article was finished, off it went to the magazines.

Jack longed to see his young friends, and often he had the urge to go to San Francisco and see George Sterling. Talking with other writers, listening to their experiences, and hearing about the tricks of the trade, he felt, would make his way easier. But he didn't go.

Somehow, he felt he had no right to associate with real authors until he had proved himself.

One afternoon he did meet the Applegarths. He told Mabel of his do-or-die determination to succeed as a writer.

She frowned slightly and said: "You do have talent, Jack, but don't you think it would be wiser to get some steady work and develop as a writer over the years?"

"No, I don't," he blurted out. "I want to make writing my way of life as soon as possible."

"But you can't always do as you like, you know."

"True," Jack admitted with a smile. "But in this country, you can come pretty close to it if you're willing to work hard enough. And that," he added, "is exactly what I intend to do."

Then one evening Jack got the courage to go to Bess Maddern's home and read her several of his Klondike stories.

"Your stories have strength," the pretty, dark-haired girl said. "I think that one you called 'The White Silence' is the finest I've ever heard. It is only a matter of time until the editors recognize you. Don't give up, Jack."

Yet, as the weeks went by, Jack often wondered if the editorial doors would ever open for him. His stories and articles were coming back now. Out of each bulky envelope Jack fished a printed rejection slip. So far, not a single editor had thought enough of his writing to offer a word of encouragement.

He said to his mother: "Sometimes I wonder if they even read my manuscripts. I suppose they do, though, judging by the coffee stains on some of the pages."

Jack went over the rejected manuscripts, revising, cutting out words, improving the stories in every way he could. Then, retyped, off they went to some other magazine.

The weeks grew into months. When odd jobs were scarce, the envelopes piled up on Jack's worktable. He could not always afford to buy the stamps which would send the stories on their travels again. His clothes grew shabbier and he saw nobody. He sold some of his textbooks and a raincoat which his father had left him. Money bought time, and that was what he needed. Every moment counted.

However, the day came when Jack realized he couldn't go on. For all his struggles, he had not earned a penny from the thousands of words he had written, nor had the editors given him the slightest reason to expect that they would ever pay him for his work. Besides, his mother was desperately worried, and Jack couldn't blame her. Odd jobs and the little she could earn would not pay the grocer.

Jack had spent Sunday afternoon on the Oakland waterfront. He had earned a dollar for painting the cabin of a sloop at the Yacht Club dock. The job done, he stopped on his way home to see Pete, the fisherman.

From the wharf shed, Pete called: "Come inside, Jack. I got hot coffee, Italian bread, and ham. Sit down and eat. How is the writing business going? Did you sell some stories?"

Jack shook his head. "It looks as if I'll have to give up writing, Pete."

"Give up? I know you better than that, Jack. You don't ever give up. Maybe you need some money to buy the paper and stamps. I can help you."

"No, thanks, Pete. I'll have to work this out my own way. I'm giving myself another week. If I don't sell something, I'll try to get on with the Fish Patrol again, or maybe go to sea. I'll save as much as I can and then go back to the typewriter again."

Pete nodded as he wrapped a big salmon in a newspaper. "You take this fish home. Fresh caught today." Thrusting the package into Jack's hands, he said, "Don't forget—sometimes it is pretty black just before dawn comes."

The next morning, Jack watched from his window as the mail carrier paused by the gate to stuff thick envelopes into the box. Rejections. Nothing but rejections. Magazine offices, he thought, must have a machine to handle the work of unknown authors. A machine which removed the story from one envelope, put it in another with a rejection slip, and sent it sailing back to its unhappy creator. But one of these days, Jack told himself grimly, that machine will break down, and then—

Tuesday and Wednesday brought more thick envelopes. More rejected stories and articles to pile up on the table for want of postage to send them out again. Four more days and the typewriter would go silent.

Thursday began like most days, except that there were no odd jobs to be had that morning and so Jack was at his worktable revising the stories which had come back the day before. A new yarn was stirring in his mind— a long one about a dog, but it was no use to begin a long story. In three days his week would be up.

Jack's mother usually brought in the mail. This morning, however, she had gone to Eliza's. So it was Jack himself who went out to see what the mail carrier had brought.

From the box he fished a thin envelope among the usual cluster of bulky ones. His fingers began to tremble. He stared, wide-eyed, at the printing in the upper left hand corner. This was from the *Overland Monthly,* a San Francisco magazine to which he had sent one of his Klondike stories. Such a slim envelope couldn't contain the story. And, if it didn't . . .

Another small envelope fluttered to the ground from the bundle of mail. This was from the *Black Cat,* an eastern magazine.

Jack dashed back to his room, his heart pounding. At the very least, letters showed that the editors were interested. Perhaps he was being asked to change the stories in some way, or to cut them down to suit the needs of the magazines.

Back at his table, he sat down. Knowing that he had let his hopes ride too high, he was almost afraid to open the envelopes. But finally, he did. He read the one from the *Overland Monthly* first. The magazine was buying his story, *The Man on the Trail* for five dollars!

Five dollars! That was as much as he could hope to earn in a week at part time jobs. Eagerly, he tore open the second letter. The *Black Cat* would be glad to publish Mr. London's story. And the amount? Could he have read aright? He rubbed his eyes and looked again. Forty dollars!

Jack leaped to his feet. He'd run to Eliza's and break the wonderful news to her and his mother. Then he'd tell Mammy Jenny and Pete and the Applegarths. Already he could see Bess Maddern's eyes lighting up when he told her.

Abruptly, at the door, he halted. He had won a little victory—but the long battle lay ahead. This was no time to go shouting his news to the skies. There was no time to waste. Besides, the new story was waiting to be written. The story of a dog he'd met in the Klondike. A big, wonderful dog, whose name was Buck.

Turning, he went back to his typewriter. He could see Buck, snatched from his comfortable home in California and harnessed to

a dog sled in the frozen north. He could hear the driver's cry, "Mush on," the crack of the whip, and the snarls of the pack. And there was Buck, leading the team of seasoned Alaskan huskies, plunging through the snowy whiteness over Chilkoot Pass.

Jack slipped a fresh sheet of paper into his typewriter and began writing:

THE CALL OF THE WILD
by
JACK LONDON

Buck did not read the newspapers, or he would have known that trouble was brewing. . . .